It's another Quality Book from CGP

This book is for anyone doing AQA A GCSE Geography at Foundation Level.

It contains lots of tricky exam-style questions designed to make you sweat — because that's the only way you'll get any better.

There are questions to see what you know. There are questions to test your geographical skills. And it's jam-packed with hints and tips — so you'll be well prepared for your exams.

We've also put some daft bits in to try and make the whole experience at least vaguely entertaining for you.

What CGP is all about

Our sole aim here at CGP is to produce the highest quality books — carefully written, immaculately presented and dangerously close to being funny.

Then we work our socks off to get them out to you — at the cheapest possible prices.

Contents

Published by CGP

Editors:
Claire Boulter, Ellen Bowness, Joe Brazier, Murray Hamilton, Karen Wells.

Proofreading:
Julie Wakeling, Eileen Worthington.

ISBN: 978 1 84762 381 2

With thanks to Laura Jakubowski for copyright research.

Graph of tiltmeter readings at Mount St Helens on page 6 © Earth Science Australia 1995-2009. www.earthsci.org

Data used to construct the graph of sulfur dioxide emissions at Mount St Helens on page 6 © U.S. Geological Survey, www.usgs.gov

Map of Mount St Helens on page 7 © Steven Dutch, University of Wisconsin-Green Bay

Map of Yellowstone National Park on page 7 © U.S. Geological Survey, www.usgs.gov

Data used to compile the graph on page 7 and the map on page 10 © U.S. Geological Survey, www.usgs.gov

Map of UK geology on page 11 reproduced by kind permission of the British Geological Survey. ©NERC. All rights reserved. IPR/119-11CT.

With thanks to Science Photo Library for permission to reproduce the photograph on page 13.

With thanks to iStockphoto.com for permission to reproduce the photographs used on pages 14, 15, 28, 39, 41, 48, 55, 73, 84 and 88.

Graphs on pages 20, 21 and 24 adapted from Crown Copyright data supplied by the Met Office.

Data used to compile the graph on page 25 adapted from Climate Change 2001: The Scientific Basis. Contribution of Working Group I
to the Third Assessment Report of the Intergovernmental Panel on Climate Change. Figure 5. Cambridge University Press

Data used to compile the table on page 26, source: http://www.direct.gov.uk/en/Motoring/OwningAVehicle/HowToTaxYourVehicle/DG_10012524 © Crown copyright

Mapping data on pages 40, 49 and 57 reproduced by permission of Ordnance Survey® on behalf of HMSO © Crown copyright (2009). All rights reserved.
Ordnance Survey® Licence No. 100034841.

Data used to compile the UK average rainfall map on page 45 from the Manchester Metropolitan University.

Data used to compile the UK population density map on page 45 from Office for National Statistics: General Register Office for Scotland, Northern Ireland Statistics
& Research Agency. © Crown copyright reproduced under the terms of the Click-Use Licence.

Data used to construct the flow map on page 67, source: International Passenger Survey, Office for National Statistics © Crown copyright reproduced under the
terms of the Click-Use Licence

Data used to compile the table on page 68 © Reuters Foundation 2002

Data used to compile the table on page 85 (except GNI per capita data) and table on page 86 © Central Intelligence Agency

Data used to compile the table on page 87 and the graph on page 89 from Human Development Report 2009 © United Nations, 2009.

Reproduced with permission & Data used to compile the graph on page 87 © United Nations, 2009.

Data use to compile the pie charts on page 88 © World Trade Organisation,
http://stat.wto.org/CountryProfile/WSDBCountryPFView.aspx?Language=E&Country=AU,BE,CA,CN,TH,UG,GB,UY,ZM,NI

Information used to compile the article on page 90 © www.kibera.net

Data use to compile the map on page 91 © www.ustr.gov

Data used to compile the article on page 92 from DFID, 'Working to reduce poverty in Ghana' © Crown copyright

Data used to compile the map on page 93 © European Communities, 1995-2009

Data used to compile the graph on page 94 © Crown copyright, reproduced under the terms of the Click-Use Licence.

Data used to compile the graph on page 97, sources: History: Energy Information Administration (EIA), 'International Energy Annual 2006'
(June-December 2008). Projections: EIA, 'World Energy Projections Plus' (2009).

Data used to compile the graph on page 100 © Crown copyright, reproduced under the terms of the Click-Use Licence.

Data used to compile the UK tourism graphs on pages 102 and 103 from Office for National Statistics: General Register Office for Scotland, Northern Ireland
Statistics & Research Agency. © Crown copyright, reproduced under the terms of the Click-Use Licence.

Groovy website: www.cgpbooks.co.uk
Printed by Elanders Ltd, Newcastle upon Tyne.
Jolly bits of clipart from CorelDRAW®

Based on the classic CGP style created by Richard Parsons.

Exam Breakdown and Answering Questions

Welcome to the wonderful world of <u>exam practice</u>. This book will help you get a bit of practice at the kind of questions they're going to throw at you in the exam. It'll also help you to figure out <u>what</u> you <u>need to revise</u> — practise the questions for the topics you've learnt in class and if there are any questions that you <u>can't answer</u> then <u>go back and revise that topic</u> some more.

There are <u>Two Exams</u> For GCSE Geography

First up, here's <u>what</u> you've got to do — we'll come on to <u>how to do it</u> in a bit.
You'll have to sit <u>two exams</u> for GCSE Geography — one for Unit 1 (<u>Physical Geography</u>)
and one for Unit 2 (<u>Human Geography</u>).

Unit 1 Exam: *Physical Geography*

Here's how it's <u>structured</u>:

1 hour 30 minutes	75 marks in total	37.5% of your final mark

- There are <u>seven</u> questions in total.
- You need to answer <u>three</u> out of the seven questions — <u>one</u> question from Section <u>A</u>, <u>one</u> question from Section <u>B</u>, then a <u>third</u> question from <u>either</u> section.

'One question' me___
a big multi-par___
beastie worth 2___
marks in total

Unit 2 Exam: *Human Geography*

f your
ark

The Unit 2 Human Geography exam is changing.

From June 2013, nine extra marks will be available for spelling, punctuation and grammar.

If you'd like more information, your teacher should be able to help.

QLGA4

<u>Pick</u> **Your** <u>Questions Carefully in the</u>

1) If you've <u>only studied three topics</u> in class for Unit 1 then it's pretty obvious that you need to answer the exam questions on those three topics.

2) But, if you've studied <u>more than three</u> you've got a bit of <u>choice</u> in the exam. Have a <u>quick look at</u> <u>ALL the questions</u> on the topics you've studied and figure out which ones are <u>easiest</u> — look at all the parts though (don't just go for one where you can answer the first part and none of the rest).

<u>Make Sure you</u> <u>Understand</u> **what the** <u>Question's Asking You to Do</u>

It's dead easy to <u>misread</u> a question and spend five minutes writing about the <u>wrong thing</u>.
Four simple tips can help you <u>avoid</u> this:

1) Figure out if it's a <u>case study question</u> — if the question wording includes 'using <u>named examples</u>' or 'with reference to one <u>named</u> area' you need to include a case study.

2) <u>Underline</u> the <u>command words</u> in the question (the ones that tell you <u>what to do</u>).

3) <u>Underline</u> the <u>key words</u> (the ones that tell you what it's <u>about</u>), e.g. volcanoes, tourism, immigrants.

4) <u>Re-read</u> the <u>question</u> and your <u>answer</u> when you've finished, just to check that what you've written really does answer the question being asked. A common mistake is to <u>miss a bit out</u> — like when questions say 'use <u>data</u> from the graph in your answer' or 'use <u>evidence</u> from the map'.

Command word	Means write about...
Describe	what it's <u>like</u>
Explain	<u>why</u> it's like that (i.e. give <u>reasons</u>)
Compare	the <u>similarities</u> AND <u>differences</u>
Contrast	the <u>differences</u>
Suggest why	give <u>reasons</u> for

Answering Questions

Some Questions _are_ Level Marked

1) For some questions you'll get marks for writing specific words or sentences — each correct one you give will be worth 1 mark, up to a maximum of four marks.

2) Other questions are level marked — your answer will be judged to be basic (level 1) or clear (level 2). The higher the level of your answer, the more marks you'll get.

3) Here's a bit about what's expected from different level answers:

Level 1 answers...	Level 2 answers...
...show you have basic knowledge and understanding of the topic. You won't have used many specialist terms (geographical words), your ideas won't be linked together and your answer won't have much structure.	...show you have good knowledge and clear understanding of the topic. You'll have used some specialist terms, structured your answer well and linked some of your ideas together.

4) Level marked questions are worth 4 or 6 marks (6 mark questions are usually case study questions). To get top marks you'll need to deliver a super duper level 2 answer.

5) You'll also be marked on your spelling, punctuation and grammar in level marked questions. The better these are the higher the level you'll get, so make sure you check your answer carefully.

> Level marked questions don't have one right answer, so you won't find full written answers for them in the answer book. Instead, there are 'hints' telling you the types of thing you need to write to get top marks.

Answers to _Case Study Questions_ **Need** Loads of Details

1) In the exam, the questions worth lots of marks almost always involve writing about a case study.

2) I know it sounds obvious, but pick a case study that you know plenty about.

3) Write yourself a mini plan of how you're going to answer the question, e.g. if the question is 'Describe the cause and impacts of a volcanic eruption you have studied' your plan might be:

- name of volcano, where it is, when it erupted
- the cause of the eruption
- primary impacts
- secondary impacts

4) Make sure you INCLUDE PLENTY OF DETAILS, e.g. place names, facts, dates etc.

Here are a Few Other Handy Hints to Remember...

1) Take a calculator into the exam — you may need to work things out that you can't do in your head.

2) A ruler and protractor are also essential for reading and drawing graphs.

3) Draw any diagrams in pencil, that way if you get something wrong you can rub it out (which reminds me... don't forget to take a rubber in too).

4) Use geographical words where you can, e.g. 'discharge' instead of 'volume and velocity of water'.

5) Use the number of marks each part of a question is worth to figure out how much time to spend on it — for every one mark you've got a little bit over one minute, e.g. if it's a 4 mark question you've got 5 minutes to answer it.

6) Do the questions that you know the answers to first and leave the trickier ones till later.

7) If you're running out of time at the end of the exam don't panic — just write what you can as bullet points. You'll still get some marks for doing this.

Tectonic Plates

1 Study **Figure 1**, which shows the Earth's tectonic plates.

Figure 1

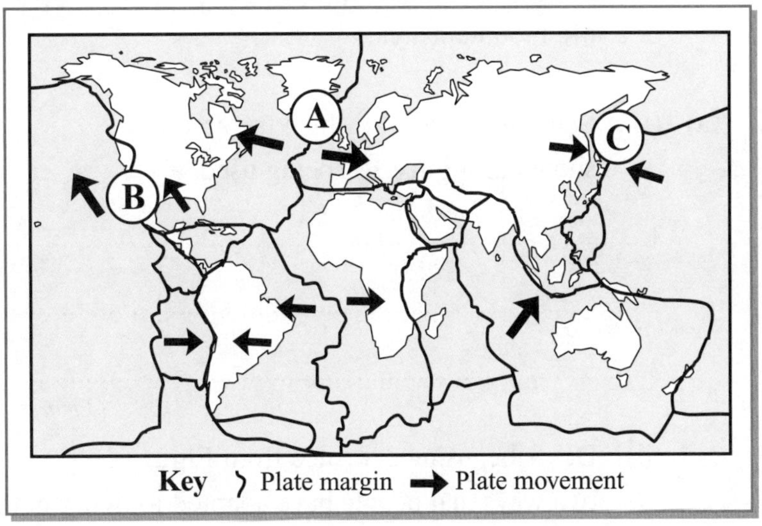

Key 〉 Plate margin ➔ Plate movement

(a) (i) Name the type of plate margin labelled A in **Figure 1**.

....

....
(1 mark)

(ii) Explain why new crust forms at this plate margin.

....

....

....
(2 marks)

(b) The San Andreas Fault is labelled B in **Figure 1**.
Crust is neither formed or destroyed at this plate margin.
What is this type of plate margin called?

....
(1 mark)

(c) At the plate margin labelled C in **Figure 1**, continental crust meets oceanic crust.
Give two ways that continental crust is different from oceanic crust.

1 ....

2 ....
(2 marks)

Figure 2

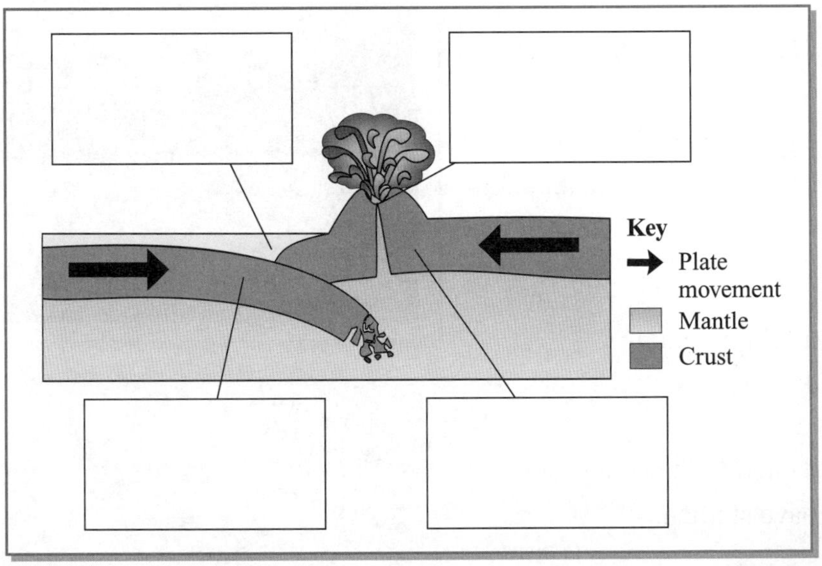

Key
➔ Plate movement
Mantle
Crust

(d) **Figure 2** is a diagram of a plate margin.

(i) What type of plate margin does it show?

....

....
(1 mark)

(ii) Label the types of plates and the features that form at the margin.
(4 marks)

Fold Mountains

1 Study **Figure 1**, which is a map of a fold mountain area.

Figure 1

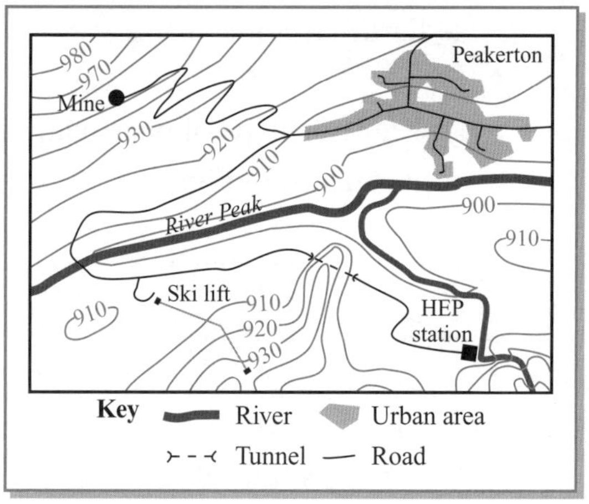

Key — River, Urban area, Tunnel, — Road

(a) (i) State three ways in which the area shown in **Figure 1** is being used.

1 ....

2 ....

3 ....

(3 marks)

(ii) Describe, using evidence from **Figure 1**, two ways that people have adapted to living in the area.

1 ....

2 ....

(2 marks)

(b) (i) At which type of plate margin can fold mountains be found?

....

(1 mark)

(ii) Describe how fold mountains are formed.

....

....

(2 marks)

(c) Study **Figure 2**, which shows the Rockies in North America. The Rockies are a fold mountain area. Describe the characteristics of fold mountain areas.

Figure 2

Use the photo to help you — say what characteristics you see.

....

....

....

....

....

(3 marks)

(d) Describe the ways in which a fold mountain area you have studied is used.

(4 marks)

(e) Describe how people have adapted to the conditions in a fold mountain area you have studied.

(6 marks)

The wording 'you have studied' tells you it's a case study question.

UK Tourism

1   Study **Figure 1**, an extract from a report into tourism in the UK.

Figure 1

A thriving tourist industry is important for a healthy economy. Data collected over a ten year period shows that the UK continues to be a popular tourist destination, with London being a major attraction for overseas tourists.
Many experts suggest the recent trend in numbers reflects the worldwide recession. The UK tourist industry can look forward to brighter times ahead though, as the 2012 Olympic Games (to be held in London) are expected to attract up to 6.6 million extra visitors to the city.

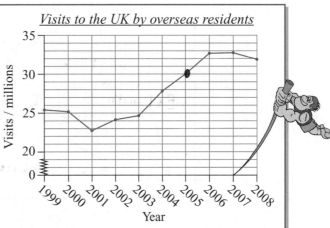

Visits to the UK by overseas residents

(a) (i)   How many visits to the UK from overseas were there in 2005?

30 million

(1 mark)

(ii)   Tick the correct box to show whether each of the following statements is **True** or **False**.

	True	False
The number of tourists visiting the UK increased from 1999 to 2008.	✓	
Fewer tourists visited the UK in 2003 than in 2000.	✓	
The number of tourists visiting the UK increased steadily from 1999 to 2004.		✓

(3 marks)

(b) (i)   Give one reason why huge numbers of tourists are attracted to London each year.

(1 mark)

(ii)   Complete the paragraph below to explain the importance of major events such as the Olympic Games to the UK's economy. Choose the correct words from this list.

tourists   jobs   money   extra   businesses   less

Major events attract .... visitors to the UK, who will spend money, helping

the economy to grow. They create a lot of .... for local people and increase

the income of .... supplying the events.

(3 marks)

(c)   Describe two factors, other than major events such as the Olympic Games, that can affect visitor numbers to the UK.

Numbers can go up or down, so the factors can be positive or negative.

1 ....

2 ....

(2 marks)

UK Tourism

2   Study **Figure 2**, which shows the life cycle of a coastal tourist resort.

Figure 2

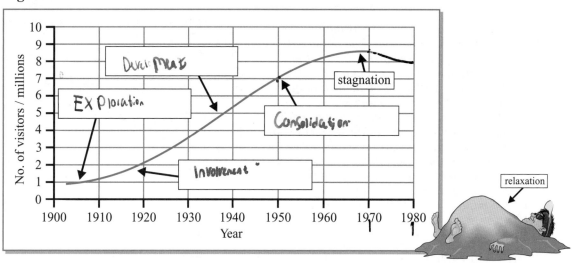

(a) (i)   Complete the boxes in **Figure 2** to show the missing labels.

Choose the correct words from the list below.

involvement   development   exploration   consolidation

(2 marks)

(ii)   Complete **Figure 2** to show that 8 million people visited in 1980.

(1 mark)

(iii)   Visitor numbers peaked at stagnation. Explain why.

....

....

....

(3 marks)

(b) (i)   How many people visited the resort in 1950?

.......7 million. Visted in 1970..

(1 mark)

(ii)   Visitor numbers declined between 1970 and 1980.
How might visitor numbers be increased?

....

(1 mark)

(c)   Draw a line to link each stage of the tourist area life cycle with the facilities available.

Exploration	Local people start providing facilities for tourists.
Involvement	There are few tourist facilities.
Development	Big companies take over the area and provide more facilities.

(2 marks)

UK Tourism

3   Study **Figure 3**, which is an extract from a report on a UK National Park.

(a) (i)   What was the maximum number of serious traffic accidents involving tourists in any one year?

....

(1 mark)

(ii)   Use **Figure 3** to describe why the National Park is a popular tourist area.

....

....

....

....

....

(2 marks)

Figure 3

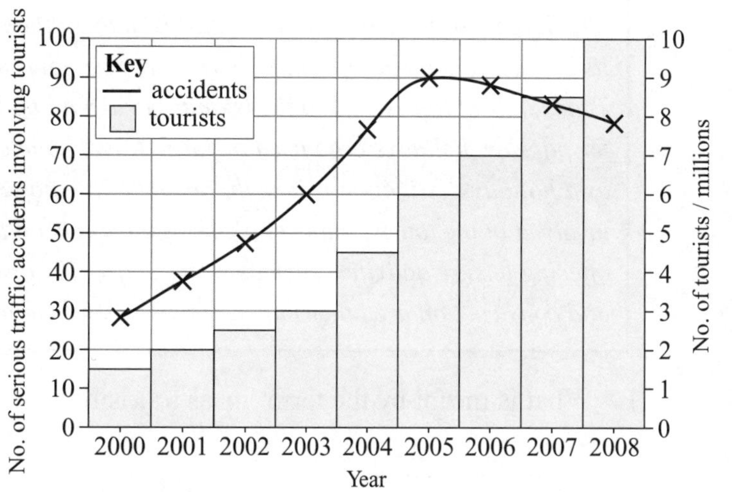

The 40 mph speed limit, introduced in 2005, hasn't put visitors off. Not surprising with all the Park has to offer — acres of moorland and woodland, with over 500 miles of footpaths and plenty of cycle routes. The rivers are open to canoeists in the winter months and they're full of wild brown trout, sea trout and salmon.

(b) (i)   Use **Figure 3** to describe three possible negative impacts of the tourists visiting the Park.

1 ....

2 ....

3 ....

(3 marks)

(ii)   Use **Figure 3** to describe one way that the Park is managing the negative impact of tourists.

....

(1 mark)

(iii)   Suggest two other ways in which the impact of tourists can be managed by National Parks.

1 ....

2 ....

(2 marks)

4   Suggest an action plan for **either** a named UK National Park **or** a named UK coastal resort that will encourage tourists to visit the area.

> Choose a case study that you know well, so you can include lots of detail in your answer.

(6 marks)

5   Describe the management strategies that are used to cope with the impact of tourists in **either** a named UK National Park **or** a named UK coastal resort.

(6 marks)

Mass Tourism

1   Study **Figure 1**, which gives information about tourism in the Seychelles.

Figure 1

The Seychelles is a collection of small islands in the Indian Ocean. Its climate and landscape make it an attractive tourist destination. Thousands of tourists fly to the islands each year, many travelling there for package holidays organised by large travel companies. Its popularity as a holiday destination means that much of the population is directly involved in the tourist industry, working in hotels and restaurants, or offering leisure activities such as water sports. Transportation, fishing and construction are other important sources of employment.

(a) (i)   What is meant by the term 'mass tourism'?

....
(1 mark)

(ii) Use **Figure 1** to describe two positive economic impacts of tourism on the Seychelles.

1 ....

2 ....
(2 marks)

(iii) Give a negative economic impact of tourism on the Seychelles.

....
(1 mark)

(b) Draw a line to link each of the statements to complete the sentences about the impact of mass tourism on the environment in the Seychelles.

Thousands of tourists flying to the island		depletes fish stocks.
Water sports using motor boats		causes air pollution.
Fishing to supply food for tourists		cause water pollution.

(2 marks)

(c) Suggest four strategies that would encourage tourists to continue visiting the Seychelles.

1 ....

2 ....

3 ....

4 ....
(4 marks)

2   Describe the impacts of mass tourism on a named tropical area, apart from the Seychelles.

(6 marks)

Tourism in Extreme Environments

1   Study **Figure 1**, which shows a page from a travel company brochure.

Figure 1

Holidays with
Extreme Adventurers
Available in 2012:

Activity \ Destination	Antarctica	Tibet	Sahara Desert
Half-day jeep tour	—	£165pp	£175pp
Two-day wildlife tour	£400pp	£385pp	—
Five-day mountain trek	—	£750pp	—
Ice climbing	£125pp	—	—

pp = per person

Prices include a 15% donation to fund local projects, which include the management of sustainably logged forests, the repair and replacement of footpaths and the removal of litter and rubbish.

(a) (i)   Using **Figure 1**, calculate the total price of a wildlife tour in Tibet for three people.

....
(1 mark)

(ii)   Describe three reasons why people go on extreme holidays.

1 ....

2 ....

3 ....
(3 marks)

(iii)   Suggest why the demand for holidays in extreme environments has increased.

....

....

There are three marks
so give three reasons.   ....
(3 marks)

(b)   Using **Figure 1**, suggest three impacts of tourism in extreme environments.

1 ....

2 ....

3 ....
(3 marks)

2   Explain the strategies used in a named extreme environment to help reduce the impacts of tourism.

Spelling and grammar are important in 6 mark questions, so check your answer.
(6 marks)

Ecotourism

1 Study **Figure 1**, an advertisement for an ecotourist destination.

(a) (i) What is meant by the term 'ecotourism'?

....

....

(1 mark)

(ii) Tick the correct box to show whether each of the following statements about the ecotourist destination advertised in **Figure 1** is **True** or **False**.

Figure 1

Ingrid's Country Lodgings

Come and stay in one of our eight cosy wooden lodges in Upper Tweedy Valley, home of the wild bears and golden eagles.
Sample the delights of our locally-produced food and drink, enjoy our hand-made arts and crafts, then dance the night away to one of our

local bands.
Or you can relax in one of our state-of-the-art, solar-powered hot tubs before snuggling into a king-size bed, made of timber from our local, sustainably managed forests.
Booking is highly recommended.
Call 0131 715723

	True	False
It uses sustainable materials.	☐	☐
It is a large-scale tourist destination.	☐	☐
It uses renewable energy.	☐	☐

(3 marks)

(b) (i) Describe one economic benefit of ecotourism.

....

(1 mark)

(ii) Describe two ways ecotourism can benefit the environment.

1 ....

2 ....

(2 marks)

(c) Complete the paragraph below to explain how ecotourism contributes to the sustainable development of the Upper Tweedy Valley. Choose the correct words from this list.

more   negative   reduces   positive   fewer   improves

Ecotourism helps the area to develop because it .... the quality of life for local

people by providing them with jobs. It is more sustainable than other forms of development

because it does not have a big .... effect on the environment, e.g. it uses solar

energy instead of fossil fuels, and it uses up .... resources, e.g. it uses wood

from sustainably managed forests.

(3 marks)

2 Choose one ecotourist destination you have studied.

Name of ecotourist destination ....

Describe the ways in which ecotourism has benefited this destination.

Think about social, economic and environmental benefits.

(6 marks)

GAFW42

Volcanoes

1   Study **Figure 1**, which shows the Earth's tectonic plates and the distribution of volcanoes.

Figure 1

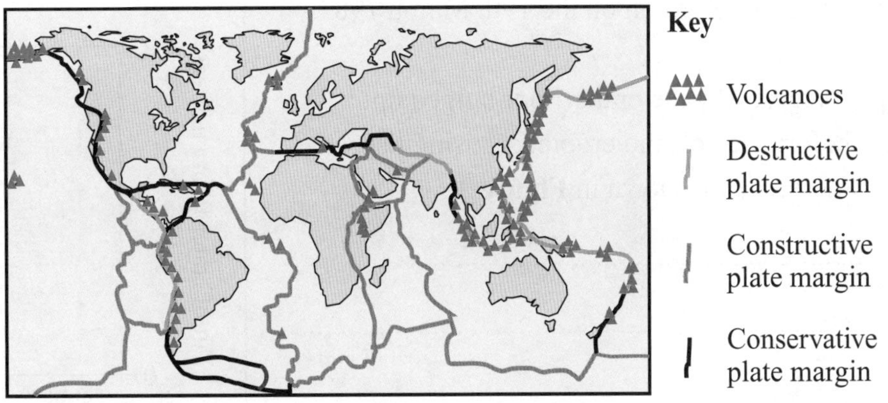

Key

▲▲▲   Volcanoes

┃   Destructive plate margin

┃   Constructive plate margin

┃   Conservative plate margin

(a) (i)   Tick the correct box to show whether each of the following statements about the distribution of volcanoes is **True** or **False**.

	True	False
Volcanoes are always found on plate margins.	☐	☐
Volcanoes are found on all three types of plate margin.	☐	☐
More volcanoes are found on constructive plate margins than destructive plate margins.	☐	☐
There is a line of volcanoes along the coast of Japan.	☐	☐

(4 marks)

(ii)   Complete the paragraph below to explain why volcanoes occur at destructive plate margins. Choose the correct words from the following list.

oceanic   vents   lava   magma   continental   chambers

The .... plate moves down into the mantle, where it's melted and destroyed.

A pool of .... forms, which then rises through cracks in the crust called

.... It then erupts onto the surface, forming a volcano.

(3 marks)

(b) Give one difference between a shield volcano and a composite volcano for each of the following characteristics.

Shape ....

....

Composition ....

....

(2 marks)

(c) For a volcanic eruption you have studied, describe the primary and secondary impacts.

(6 marks)

Volcanoes

2   Study **Figure 3**, which shows measurements made
     by scientists on Mount St. Helens in the USA,
     before a minor eruption on the 19th March 1982.

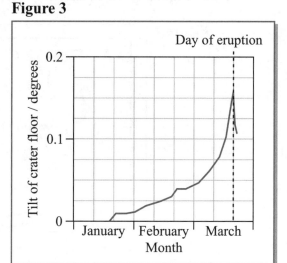

Figure 3

(a) (i)   Suggest why the crater floor bulged up
           before the volcano erupted, causing the
           increased tilt shown in **Figure 3**.

    ....

    ....
                                                    (1 mark)

    (ii)   Describe what happened to the tilt of the crater
           floor after the eruption.

    ....
                                                                                                                        (1 mark)

Figure 4

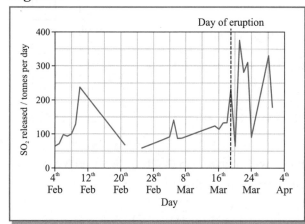

(b) Study **Figure 4**, which shows
    measurements of sulfur dioxide
    emissions made on Mount St. Helens.

    (i)   How much sulfur dioxide was
           released on the day of the eruption?

    ....
                                                    (1 mark)

    Draw your own lines
    on graphs in the exam
    to help you read them.

    (ii)   Complete **Figure 4** to show that 100 tonnes of
           sulfur dioxide were released on 24th February.
                                                    (1 mark)

(c) (i)   Which measurement (the tilt of the crater floor or the release of sulfur
           dioxide) gave a better warning of when the volcano was going to erupt?

    ....
                                                                                                                        (1 mark)

    (ii)   Give one reason for your answer to (c) (i).

    ....
                                                                                                                        (1 mark)

(d) Suggest one other way that scientists could monitor a volcano to predict when it will erupt.

    ....
                                                                                                                        (1 mark)

(e) For a named volcanic eruption, describe the immediate and long-term responses to the eruption.
                                                                                                                        (6 marks)

Supervolcanoes

1   Study **Figure 1**, which shows contour maps of Mount St. Helens (a volcano) and Yellowstone National Park (a supervolcano).

Figure 1

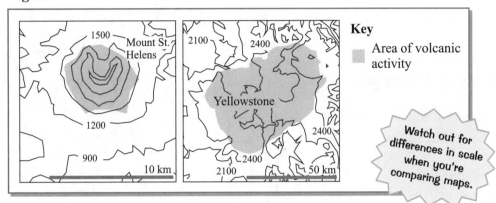

Watch out for differences in scale when you're comparing maps.

(a)   Tick the correct box to show whether each of the following statements is **True** or **False**.

	True	False
Supervolcanoes are usually mountains.	☐	☐
Mount St. Helens is lower than 1500 m in height.	☐	☐
The Yellowstone National Park supervolcano covers more than three times the area of Mount St. Helens.	☐	☐
Supervolcanoes have a caldera, not a crater.	☐	☐

(4 marks)

(b)   **Figure 2** shows the volume of lava that erupted from some volcanoes and supervolcanoes.

Figure 2

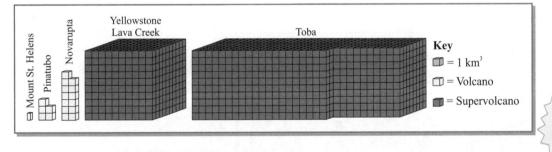

Key
☐ = 1 km³
☐ = Volcano
▨ = Supervolcano

Don't forget to include the units.

(i)   How much lava erupted from Novarupta? ....
(1 mark)

(ii)   Using **Figure 2**, compare the volume of lava ejected by volcanoes and supervolcanoes.

....

....
(2 marks)

(iii)   Suggest one other way in which the effects of supervolcanoes are different from volcanoes.

....

....
(2 marks)

Earthquakes

1 Study **Figure 1**, which shows the Earth's tectonic plates and the distribution of earthquakes.

(a) Tick the correct box to show whether each of the following statements about the distribution of earthquakes is **True** or **False**.

Figure 1

	True	False
Almost all earthquakes occur at plate margins.	✓	
Some earthquakes occur in the middle of plates.		
Earthquakes don't occur at constructive plate margins.		

(3 marks)

Key: Earthquakes | Conservative plate margin | Destructive plate margin | Constructive plate margin

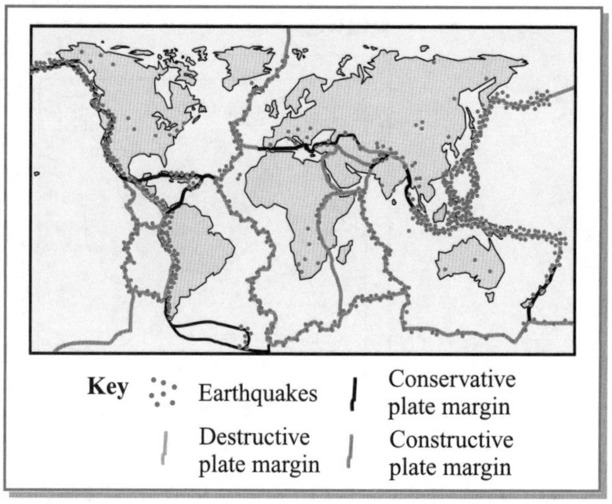

(b) Complete the paragraph below to explain why earthquakes occur at destructive plate margins. Choose the correct words from the following list.

down   up   mantle   core   increases   decreases

One plate can get stuck as it's moving .... past the

other into the .... Tension ...*increases*...... until the

plates eventually jerk past each other, sending out shockwaves.

(3 marks)

2 Study **Figure 2**, which shows the focus of the 1994 Northridge earthquake in California, USA.

Figure 2

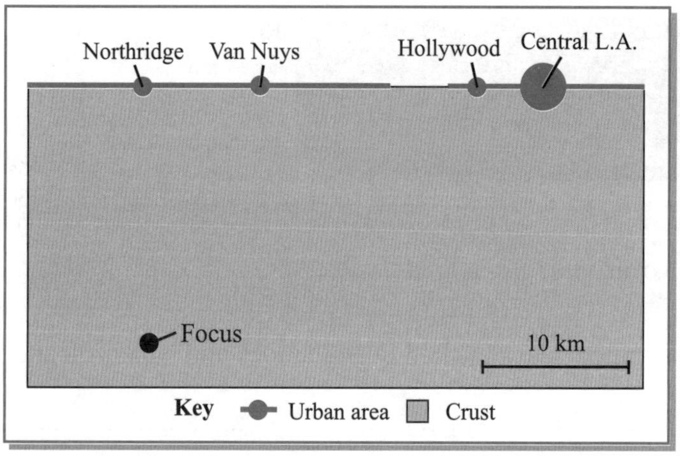

Northridge   Van Nuys   Hollywood   Central L.A.

Focus   10 km

Key: Urban area   Crust

(a) (i) Define the term 'focus'.

....

....

....

(1 mark)

(ii) How deep in the Earth was the focus of this earthquake?

....

(1 mark)

Use the scale and a ruler to answer this question.

(b) Label the epicentre of the earthquake on **Figure 2**.

(1 mark)

(c) Shockwaves from the earthquake caused damage up to 125 km away. What are shockwaves?

....

(1 mark)

Earthquakes

3 In 2008 there was an earthquake in Sichuan, China, that measured 7.9 on the Richter scale.

(a) (i) Describe how earthquakes are measured using the Richter scale.

....

....

(2 marks)

(ii) The Richter scale is logarithmic. How much more powerful is an earthquake with a magnitude of 8 compared to an earthquake with a magnitude of 7?

....

(1 mark)

(b) (i) Study **Figure 3**, which shows how the Richter scale relates to the Mercalli scale. Describe the damage you would have expected to see after the earthquake in Sichuan.

....

....

....

(1 mark)

(ii) How is the Mercalli scale measured?

....

....

....

(1 mark)

(c) Describe the primary and secondary impacts of an earthquake in a rich part of the world that you have studied.

(6 marks)

Make sure you describe the primary AND secondary impacts — you have to cover both to get top marks.

Figure 3

The Richter scale	The Mercalli scale	
1	1	Only detected by instruments
2	2	Only felt by people at rest indoors
	3	Felt by people indoors
3	4	Felt by many people, dishes and windows rattle
4	5	Felt by most people, dishes and windows broken
5	6	Felt by everyone, many objects moved
	7	Some structural damage
6	8	Heavy structural damage
7	9	Massive structural damage, some buildings destroyed
	10	All buildings damaged, many destroyed
8	11	Most buildings destroyed
9+	12	Total destruction

4 Describe the preparation for and immediate responses to an earthquake in a poor part of the world that you have studied.

(6 marks)

Tsunamis

1   **Figure 1** is a newspaper extract describing a tsunami that hit Papua New Guinea in 1998.

Figure 1

Tsunami Devastates Papua New Guinea

Over 2000 people estimated killed

Thousands homeless as villages destroyed

The coast of Papua New Guinea was hit by waves over 10 metres high on Friday evening. A string of villages along a thin strip of land between Sissano Lagoon and the Pacific Ocean were completely flattened. The tsunami was thought to be caused by a huge underwater landslide triggered by a magnitude 7.1 earthquake. The tsunami drowned many people and destroyed houses, schools and fishing boats. It also felled a large number of coconut trees along the coastline. Surviving families have fled inland, unwilling to return to the sea to fish and fearing the spread of disease. Rescue workers fear that the water could be contaminated for months to come.

(a)   Using **Figure 1**, describe one economic impact and one environmental impact of the tsunami.

Economic impact ....

Environmental impact ....

(2 marks)

(b)   Study **Figure 2**, which shows the locations hit by the tsunami and the height of the waves at that place. Coastal villages between Arnold River and Malol were heavily damaged by waves.

Figure 2

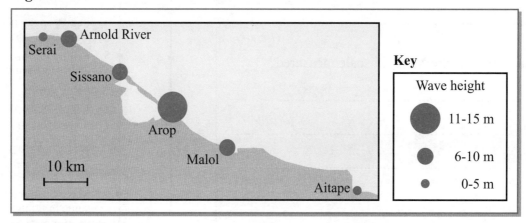

(i)   What length of coastline was hit by waves high enough to heavily damage villages?

....

(1 mark)

(ii)   How high did waves have to be to heavily damage villages?...

(1 mark)

(iii) Which area was hit by the tallest waves?..

(1 mark)

(c)   Describe the cause and effects of a tsunami you have studied.

(6 marks)

(d)   Describe the responses to a tsunami you have studied.

(6 marks)

Types of Rock

1   Study **Figure 1**, which shows the distribution of the three rock types in the UK.

(a) (i)   Use **Figure 1** to identify the most common rock type in the UK.

....
(1 mark)

Figure 1

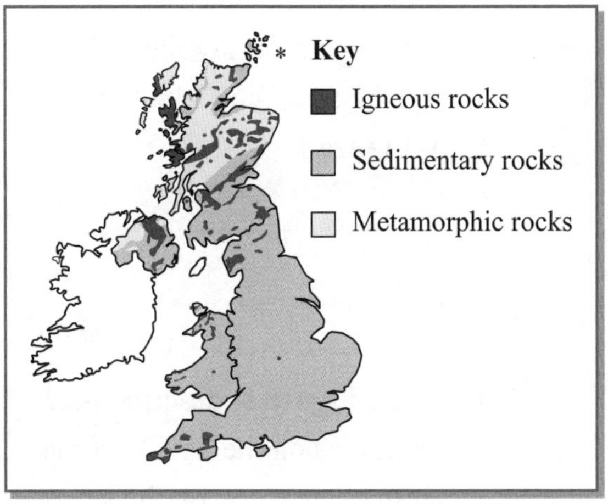

Key
- Igneous rocks
- Sedimentary rocks
- Metamorphic rocks

(ii)   Describe how this rock type is formed.

....

....

....

....
(2 marks)

Make sure you check the figure as you read each statement.

(iii)   Tick the correct box to show whether each of the following statements about the distribution of igneous rocks in the UK is **True** or **False**.

	True	False
Areas of igneous rocks can be found throughout Scotland.	☐	☐
Large areas of igneous rocks can be found on the east coast of England.	☐	☐
Some areas of igneous rocks are found around the north of Wales.	☐	☐
There are igneous rocks in the north west and south west of England.	☐	☐

(4 marks)

(b) (i)   Describe how igneous rocks are formed.

....
(1 mark)

(ii)   Complete the paragraph below to explain why the texture of intrusive igneous rock is different from the texture of extrusive igneous rock.
Choose the correct words from the following list.

coarse	**soft**	**slowly**	**compact**
fine	**quickly**	**layered**	**hard**

Intrusive igneous rock forms under the Earth's surface where magma cools down very

.... This forms large crystals that give the rock a .... texture.

Extrusive igneous rock forms on the Earth's surface where magma cools down very

.... This forms small crystals that give the rock a .... texture.

(4 marks)

The Rock Cycle

1   Study **Figure 1**, which shows the rock cycle.

(a)   (i)   Process A acting on magma creates rock type B.
Name the process labelled A and the rock type labelled B in **Figure 1**.

Figure 1

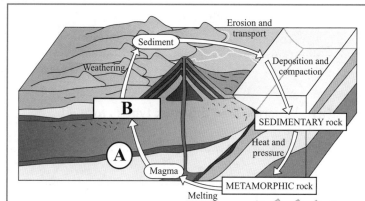

A: ....

B: ....

(2 marks)

> The rock cycle can be shown in lots of different ways so it might not look like this in your exam.

(ii)   Using **Figure 1**, describe how sediments on the land become sedimentary rock on the sea bed.

....

....

....

(2 marks)

(iii)   Using **Figure 1**, describe the formation of metamorphic rocks.

....

(1 mark)

(b)   **Figure 2** shows the most recent geological time periods.

Figure 2

Geological period	Began, million years before present
Quaternary	2.6
Tertiary	65
Cretaceous	145
Jurassic	215
Triassic	245
Permian	285
Carboniferous	360
Devonian	410
Silurian	440
Ordovician	505
Cambrian	585

(i)   How much time passed between the beginning of the Carboniferous and the Cretaceous period?

....

....

....

(1 mark)

(ii)   Complete **Figure 2** to show the geological period in which each of the following four rocks was formed across the UK:

granite   **clay**   **chalk**   **Carboniferous limestone**

> Even if you don't know the right answers it's worth guessing — you won't lose any marks.

(4 marks)

Weathering

1   **Figure 1** shows some weathered rocks in a dry desert.

Figure 1

SINCLAIR STAMMERS / SCIENCE PHOTO LIBRARY

(a) (i)   Name the type of mechanical weathering that's likely to have affected the rocks in **Figure 1**.

....
(1 mark)

(ii)   Describe how this type of weathering breaks rocks down.

....

....

....

....

(3 marks)

(iii) Name another type of mechanical weathering.

....
(1 mark)

(b) (i)   Contrast chemical weathering with mechanical weathering.

....

....
(2 marks)

(ii)   Describe the process of carbonation weathering.

....

....
(2 marks)

(iii) Name another type of chemical weathering.

....
(1 mark)

(c) (i)   What is biological weathering?

....
(1 mark)

(ii)   Give two examples of biological weathering.

1 ....

2 ....
(2 marks)

Unit 1A — Rocks, Resources and Scenery

Rocks and Landscapes

1   Study **Figure 1**, which is a photograph of a landscape.

(a) (i)   What type of rock is the landscape
in **Figure 1** based on?

Figure 1

....
(1 mark)

(ii) On **Figure 1**, label **two**
characteristics of the landscape.
(2 marks)

©iStockphoto.com/Lachlan Currie

(b) The rock in **Figure 1** has lots of joints that
aren't evenly spread. Describe how these
joints result in the formation of tors.

....

....

....

....
(3 marks)

2   Study **Figure 2**, which is a diagram of a chalk and clay landscape.

Figure 2

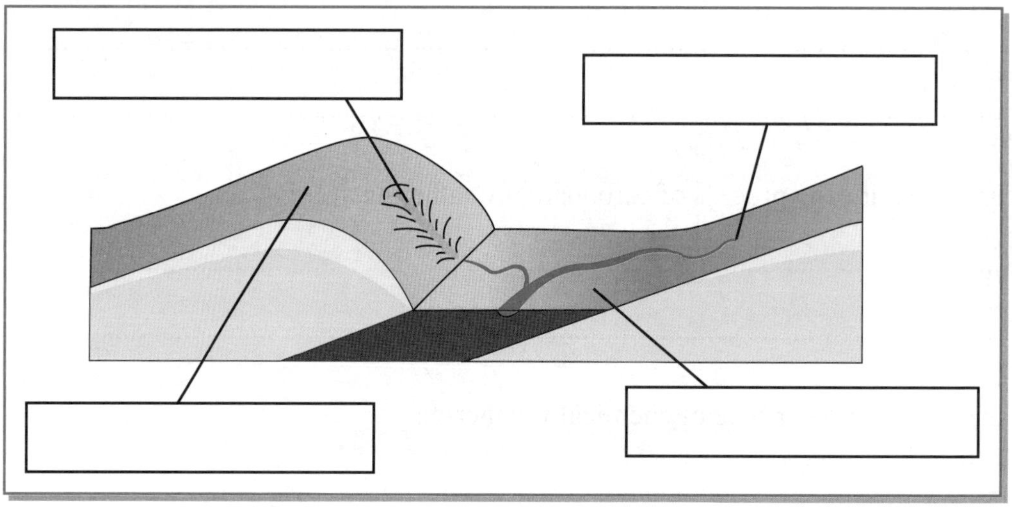

(a) Complete the boxes in **Figure 2** to show the missing labels.
(4 marks)

(b) Explain why spring lines form in a chalk and clay landscape.

....

....

....
(3 marks)

Rocks and Landscapes

3   Study **Figure 3**, which shows a gorge in a Carboniferous limestone landscape.

Figure 3

©iStockphoto.com

(a)   The gorge in **Figure 3** used to be a cavern.

   (i)   Describe how the cavern could have formed.

....

....

....

....

....
(3 marks)

  (ii)   Explain how the cavern turned into the gorge.

....
(1 mark)

(b)   (i)   Describe the formation of stalactites and stalagmites.

....

....
(2 marks)

  (ii)   Name the underground feature formed when a stalactite and a stalagmite join together.

....
(1 mark)

(c)   **Figure 4** is a diagram of a limestone landscape.
Label **Figure 4** to show **four** features of the landscape.

Keep labels clear and make sure you mark each feature with its own label.

(4 marks)

Figure 4

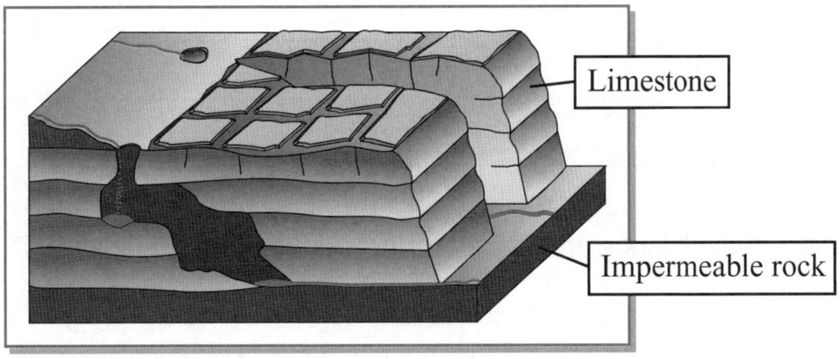

Limestone

Impermeable rock

(d)   (i)   What are resurgent rivers?

....
(1 mark)

  (ii)   Give one fact about limestone that results in the formation of dry valleys.

....
(1 mark)

Using Landscapes

1   **Figure 1** is a table of data which shows the number of different farms in a granite landscape in the UK in 1990 and 2005. **Figure 2** is a graph made from the data in **Figure 1**.

Figure 1

	1990	2005
Farm type	Number of holdings	
Livestock (cattle and sheep)	820	650
Dairy	250	110
Cereals	40	60
TOTAL	1110	820

Figure 2

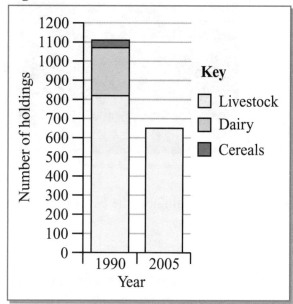

(a) (i)   Use **Figure 1** to complete **Figure 2**.

(2 marks)

Make sure the top of your bar is at the total number of holdings — if it's not, check for mistakes.

(ii) Tick the correct box to show whether each of the following statements about the pattern of farming in this area in 1990 is **True** or **False**.

	True	False
There were more than triple the number of livestock holdings compared to dairy holdings.	☐	☐
There were ten times the number of livestock holdings compared to cereal farms.	☐	☐
Livestock holdings outnumbered cereal farms because the soil in granite landscapes is acidic and waterlogged.	☐	☐

(3 marks)

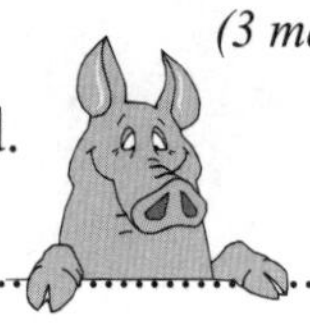

(b) Apart from farming, describe two other ways that granite landscapes can be used.

....

....

(2 marks)

(c) Why are chalk landscapes useful for providing a water supply?

....

....

(2 marks)

2   For **either** a chalk and clay **or** a granite landscape that you have studied, describe how the area has been used for farming and other activities. Circle the one you choose to write about.

Chalk and clay   **Granite**

(6 marks)

Using Landscapes

3   Study **Figure 3**, which shows the number of tourists that visited different national parks in Boulderland in 2008.

Make sure you know how to use a protractor before you go into your exam.

(a) (i)   Using **Figure 3**, calculate the number of tourists that visited the limestone landscape.

Figure 3

Key

■ The Blackboard District (chalk landscape)

▨ Worktop Moor (granite landscape)

□ Citrus View (limestone landscape)

▨ Other attractions

Total number of tourists = 6 million

....

....

....

....

(2 marks)

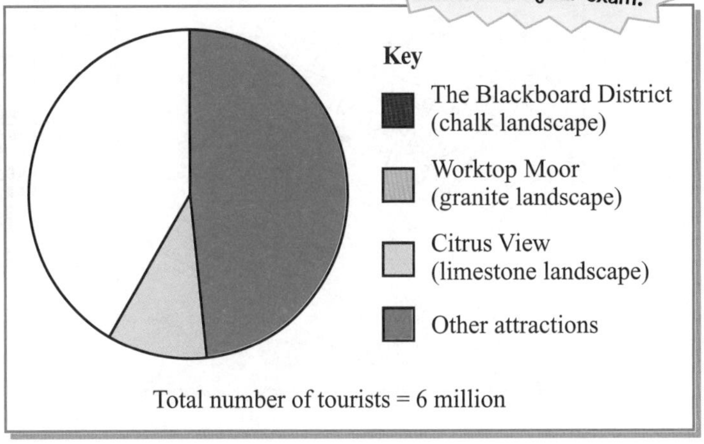

(ii) In 2008, 1 million tourists visited Worktop Moor and 1.5 million tourists visited The Blackboard District. Complete **Figure 3** to show this, and show your working.

....

(2 marks)

(b) Give two uses of quarried limestone.

1 ....

2 ....

(2 marks)

(c) Describe why limestone landscapes are popular tourist attractions.

....

....

(2 marks)

(d) (i)   Suggest two benefits of tourism in scenic landscapes.

1 ....

2 ....

(2 marks)

(ii) Suggest three costs of tourism in scenic landscapes.

1 ....

2 ....

3 ....

(3 marks)

4   Using named examples, describe how different rock landscapes are used for tourism.

(6 marks)

Quarrying Impacts

1   Study **Figure 1** and **Figure 2**, which show the front page of a newspaper
and an aerial plan of a proposed limestone quarry near the town of Himilton.

Figure 1

Figure 2

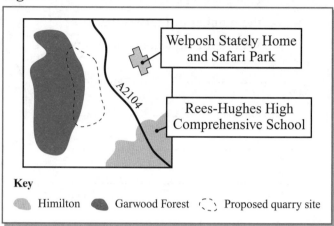

(a) (i)   Using evidence from **Figure 1** and **Figure 2**, describe one economic advantage
of the proposed quarry.

....

....
(1 mark)

(ii)   Describe two disadvantages of the proposed quarry.

1 ....

....

2 ....

....
(2 marks)

> Study the figures carefully — they'll help you get the right answers.

(b) Study **Figure 3**, which shows the estimated volume of
limestone that will be extracted from the quarry each year.

The proposed site contains 400 000 m³ of limestone.
How much limestone would be left at the site
by the end of year 3 if the quarry was in use?

....
(1 mark)

Figure 3

Year	Estimated volume of limestone extracted / m³
1	55 000
2	100 000
3	110 000
4	75 000

(c) Suggest a use for the quarry site after it has been closed down.

....
(1 mark)

2   Describe the economic, social and environmental disadvantages
of a quarry that you have studied.

(6 marks)

Quarrying Management

1   Study **Figure 1**, which shows extracts from three articles about Tunstead Quarry, Derbyshire.

(a) (i)   What is the meaning of the term 'sustainable management'?

Figure 1

Trials have shown that chips of old rubber tyres can be used to replace around 50% of the fossil fuels used to run the cement kiln at Tunstead.

NEW RAIL SERVICE TO REPLACE 24 000 LORRY TRIPS
Funding secures new facilities

In 2004, a new cement processing plant was opened at Tunstead Quarry. The plant is 40% more energy efficient and it produces 60% fewer sulfur dioxides and 9% fewer nitrogen oxides.

....

....

....

....

....

....

....

(2 marks)

(ii) Give three pieces of evidence from **Figure 1** to show that Tunstead Quarry is becoming more sustainable.

1 ....

....

2 ....

....

3 ....

....

(3 marks)

(b) Quarries can also be sustainably managed by restoring natural habitats after the quarry closes.

(i)   Explain why this is a sustainable management strategy.

....

(1 mark)

(ii) Suggest ways that the restored parts of a quarry could be used.

....

....

(2 marks)

2   For a quarry that you have studied, describe the sustainable management strategies that are being used there.

(6 marks)

UK Climate

1   Study **Figures 1** and **2**. **Figure 1** shows climate graphs for two places in the UK.
    Figure 2 shows the location of these two places in the UK.

Figure 1

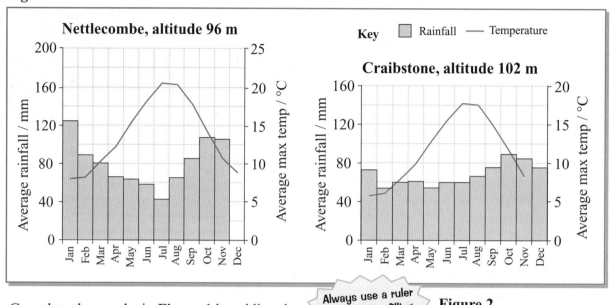

(a)   Complete the graphs in **Figure 1** by adding the
      following data to them:

Always use a ruler when you're filling in lines and bars on graphs.

Figure 2

    (i)   The average December rainfall in
        Nettlecombe is 129 mm.
(1 mark)

    (ii) The average maximum December
         temperature in Craibstone is 6.4 °C.
(1 mark)

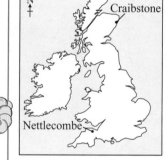

(b)   Tick the box next to the sentence that best describes
      the differences in climate between Nettlecombe and Craibstone.

    Nettlecombe is generally wetter and colder than Craibstone throughout the year.   ☐

    Craibstone is generally drier and colder than Nettlecombe throughout the year.   ☐

    Nettlecombe is always drier and colder than Craibstone throughout the year.   ☐

(1 mark)

(c) (i)   Using **Figure 2**, explain one reason for the difference in
        average monthly temperature between Nettlecombe and Craibstone.

....

....

....

(2 marks)

UK Climate

(ii)   Using **Figure 2**, explain one reason for the difference in
average monthly rainfall between Nettlecombe and Craibstone.

....

....

....

(2 marks)

2   Study **Figure 3**, which shows climate graphs for the whole of the UK.

Figure 3

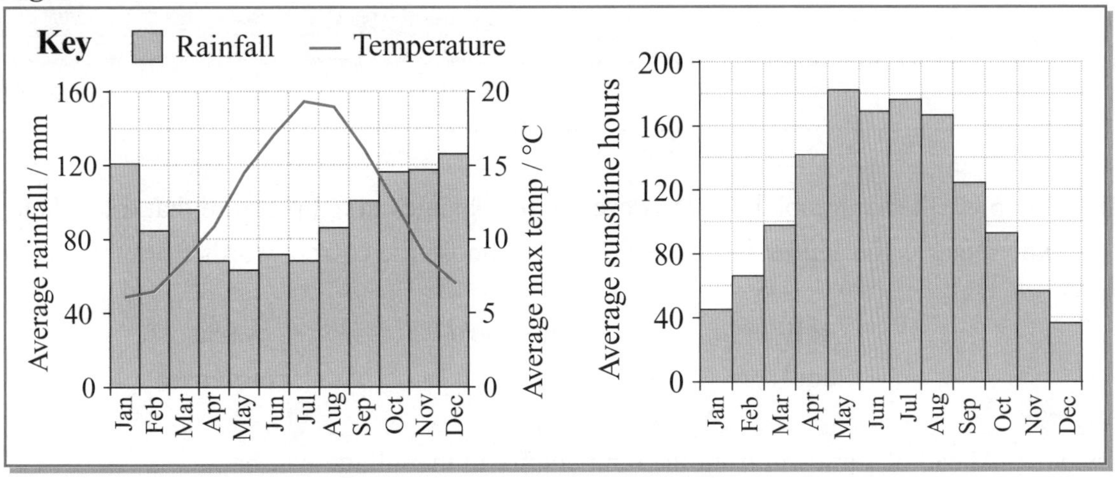

(a) (i)   In what month does the UK get the highest amount of rainfall?

....

(1 mark)

(ii)   How many sunshine hours are there on average in October in the UK?

....

(1 mark)

(b) Draw a line to link **each** of the statements to complete the sentences describing the UK's climate.

The UK's average number of sunshine hours is	highest in May.
The UK's average maximum temperature is	highest in January and December.
The UK's average rainfall is	highest in July.

Drawn the lines in pencil so you can rub them out if you make a mistake.

(2 marks)

(c) Give one factor that explains why the UK has a mild climate with both wet and dry weather.

....

(1 mark)

Depressions and Anticyclones

1   Study **Figure 1**, which shows a depression approaching a village.

(a) (i)   Complete the key in **Figure 1**.

(1 mark)

Figure 1

(ii) Describe how a depression forms.

....

....

....

....

....

....

(4 marks)

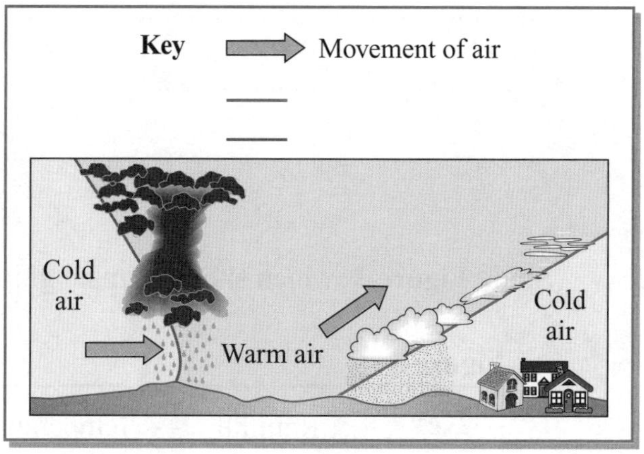

(b) Complete the paragraph below to describe the changes in temperature that the village would experience as the depression passes over it. Choose the correct words from this list.

fall	**below zero**	**warm**
cool	**rise**	**condense**

Ahead of the warm front the temperature in the village will be ....

It will then .... as the warm front passes overhead, then it will be

.... after the warm front has passed. As the cold front passes the

temperature will ....

(4 marks)

2   Study **Figure 2**, which shows the average air pressure in Derby over a period of six weeks.

Figure 2

Week	1	2	3	4	5	6
Pressure (mbar)	990	998	1008	1004	1036	1006

(a) In which week did an anticyclone pass over Derby? ....

(1 mark)

(b) Explain the weather caused by anticyclones in summer and in winter.

Summer ....

....

Winter ....

....

(4 marks)

Extreme UK Weather

1   Study **Figure 1**, which is an article about the climate of the UK.

Figure 1

> ### UK feels the heat of climate change
> Average temperature in the UK is increasing. Between 1995 and 2004, the UK had six of the ten warmest years since 1861. The hottest temperature ever recorded in the UK was in 2003 — it reached 38.5 °C in Kent. Rainfall is also increasing — the summer of 2007 was the wettest on record and rainfall is also becoming more intense.

(a) (i) Using **Figure 1**, give two pieces of evidence that UK temperature is becoming more extreme.

1 ....

....

2 ....

(2 marks)

(ii) Suggest two extreme weather events that the changes described in **Figure 1** could cause.

....

(2 marks)

(b) Describe one negative impact of extreme weather on each of transport, agriculture and people's homes and lives.

Transport ....

Agriculture ....

People's homes and lives ....

(3 marks)

(c) (i) How can warning systems reduce the negative impacts of extreme weather?

....

(1 mark)

(ii) Describe two other ways of reducing the negative impacts of extreme weather.

This question is level marked so check your spelling, punctuation and grammar.

....

....

....

....

....

(4 marks)

(d) Suggest two positive impacts that extreme weather may have on agriculture in the UK.

....

....

....

(2 marks)

Global Climate Change — Debate

1   Study **Figure 1**, which shows global temperature between 1860 and 2000.

(a) What is climate change?

....

....

....

....
(1 mark)

Figure 1

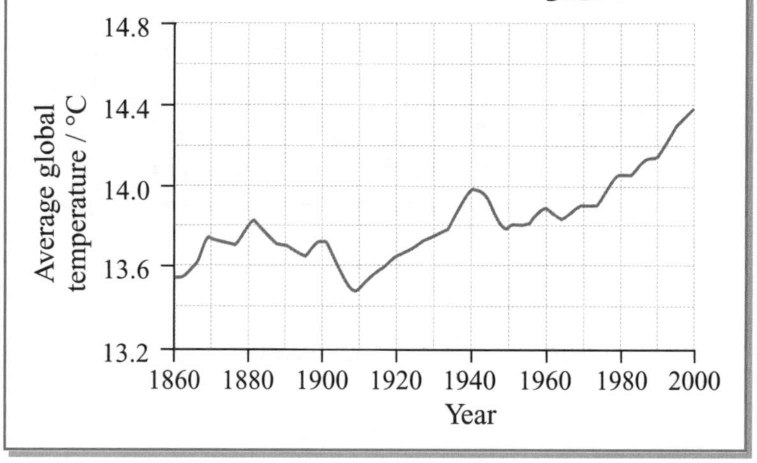

(b) (i)   How much did global temperature rise by between 1860 and 2000?

....
(1 mark)

Remember to quote figures from the graph.

(ii) Describe the change in average global temperature shown by the graph.

....

....
(2 marks)

(c) Describe one other source of evidence that shows an increase in global temperature.

....
(1 mark)

(d) There is a scientific consensus that global warming is caused by human activity.

(i)   Complete the paragraph below to explain how human activity has caused global warming. Choose the correct words from this list.

greenhouse gases	glaciation	CFCs	global warming
oceans	atmosphere	animals	fossil fuels

Carbon dioxide (CO_2) and methane (CH_4) are .... They trap heat reflected off the Earth's surface and keep the Earth warm. An increase in human activities like burning ...., farming and deforestation has caused an increase in the concentration of CO_2 and CH_4 in the .... This increase is causing ....
(4 marks)

(ii) Give one other factor that can cause the Earth's climate to change.

....
(1 mark)

Global Climate Change — Impacts

1   Study **Figure 1**, which shows data on sea level rise between 1900 and 2100.

Figure 1

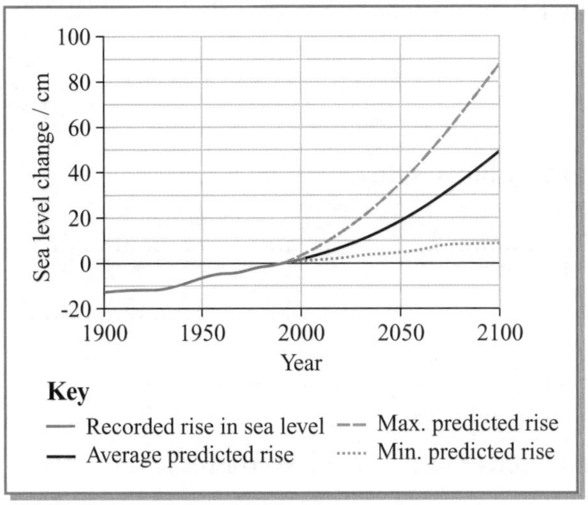

Key

— Recorded rise in sea level   -- Max. predicted rise
— Average predicted rise   ···· Min. predicted rise

(a) Sea level rise is caused by global warming. State one global environmental impact of sea level rise.

....

....

(1 mark)

(b) What is the average predicted rise in sea level between 2050 and 2100?

.... cm

(1 mark)

(c) Apart from sea level rise, give two other global environmental impacts of global warming.

....

....

(2 marks)

2   Study **Figure 2**, which shows the maize yield for a low latitude farm in Central Africa.

Figure 2

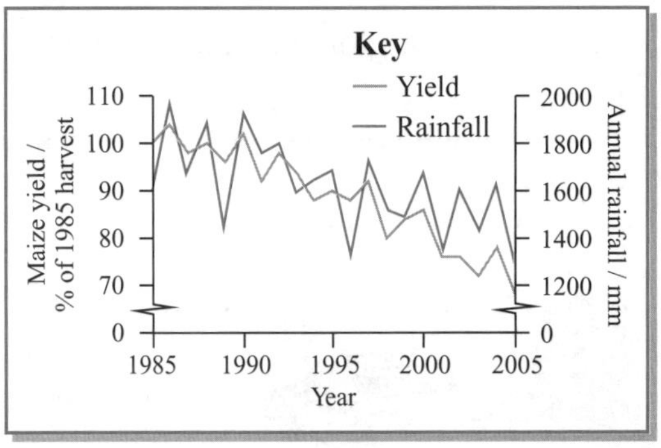

(a) (i)   Describe the trends shown in **Figure 2**.

....

....

....

....

(2 marks)

(ii)   Suggest one economic and one social impact of the trends shown in **Figure 2**.

Economic ....

Social ....

(2 marks)

(b) Give two economic and two environmental impacts of climate change in the UK.

Economic ....

Make sure the impacts you write about are specific to the UK.

....

Environmental ....

....

(4 marks)

Global Climate Change — Responses

1 The Kyoto Protocol is an international response to climate change.

(a) (i) What have countries that have signed the Kyoto Protocol agreed to do?

....

(1 mark)

(ii) Describe two ways that countries can earn carbon credits.

....

....

....

(2 marks)

(iii) Describe one factor that might limit the effectiveness of the Kyoto Protocol as a response to climate change.

....

(1 mark)

(b) Study **Figure 1**, which shows the price of car tax for cars with different CO_2 emissions. Explain how **Figure 1** shows a national response to reduce the threat of global climate change.

Figure 1

CO_2 emissions (g/km)	12 months tax (£)
111-120	35.00
121-130	120.00
131-140	120.00
141-150	125.00
151-165	150.00
166-175	175.00
176-185	175.00
186-200	215.00
201-225	215.00
226-255	405.00

....

....

....

....

(2 marks)

(c) (i) How does recycling reduce the threat of climate change?

....

(1 mark)

(ii) Suggest one way that local authorities can increase the amount of waste that is recycled.

....

(1 mark)

(iii) Describe one other local response to climate change.

....

....

....

(2 marks)

Tropical Storms

1   Study **Figure 1**, which shows a cross section of a tropical storm.

   (a) (i) Fill in the boxes in **Figure 1** to show **four** characteristics of a tropical storm.

                       (4 marks)

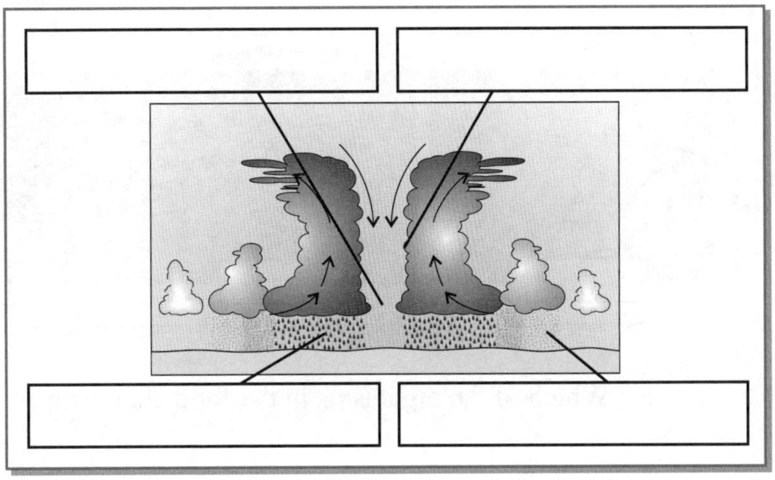

      (ii) Give two other characteristics of tropical storms.

....

....

....

....
(2 marks)

Figure 1

   (b) Study **Figure 2**, which shows the distribution of tropical storms and sea surface temperature.

Figure 2

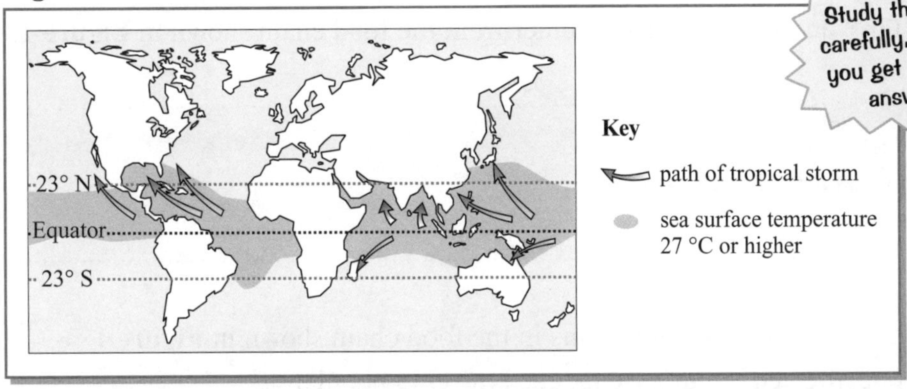

Key

↞   path of tropical storm

⬤   sea surface temperature 27 °C or higher

Study the figure carefully, it'll help you get the right answers.

Tick the correct box to show whether each of the following statements is **True** or **False**.

                                             True **False**

Tropical storms form near the equator, then move westwards and away from the equator.   ☐ ☐

Tropical storms only form over water that's cooler than 27 °C.   ☐ ☐

South-east Asia isn't affected by tropical storms.   ☐ ☐

Tropical storms affect the east coast of the USA and parts of South America and central America.   ☐ ☐

(4 marks)

   (c) Why do tropical storms lose strength when they move over land?

....
(1 mark)

2   Describe the short and long-term responses to a tropical storm that you have studied.

(6 marks)

Unit 1A — The Living World

Ecosystems

1   Study **Figure 1**, which shows a coastal food chain.

Figure 1

©iStockphoto.com/Paul Rogers

Seaweed   Periwinkle   Crab   Octopus

(a) (i)   Which of the organisms in the food chain shown in **Figure 1** is the producer?

....

(1 mark)

(ii)   What is meant by the term 'consumer'?

....

(1 mark)

(iii) Give an example of a consumer from the food chain shown in **Figure 1**.

....

(1 mark)

(b) What does a food web show?

....

(1 mark)

(c) Describe how the other organisms in the food chain shown in **Figure 1**
     might be affected if a disease reduced the crab population.

Octopus ....

Periwinkle ....

Seaweed ....

(3 marks)

(d) Describe how nutrients are cycled between the soil, plants and animals in ecosystems.

....

Make sure your
answer covers all of
the things mentioned
in the question.

....

....

....

....

(4 marks)

World Ecosystems

1   Study **Figure 1**, which shows the global distribution of tropical rainforests.

Figure 1

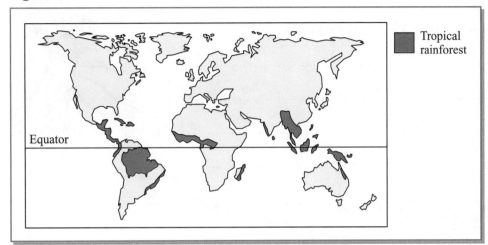

(a)   Tick the correct box to show whether each of the following statements about the distribution of tropical rainforests is **True** or **False**.

	True	False
Tropical rainforests are mainly found close to the equator.	☐	☐
There are large tropical rainforests in the USA and Europe.	☐	☐
Tropical rainforests are found in areas with a hot, wet climate.	☐	☐
Australia has no tropical rainforests.	☐	☐

(4 marks)

(b)   Describe the four vegetation layers in a tropical rainforest.

....

....

....

....

(4 marks)

(c)   Explain two ways in which rainforest plants are adapted to their environment.

1 ....

....

> There are four marks available here so make sure you describe two ways and explain them both.

....

2 ....

....

(4 marks)

Unit 1A — The Living World

World Ecosystems

2   Study **Figure 2**, which shows a diagram of a desert cactus.

Figure 2

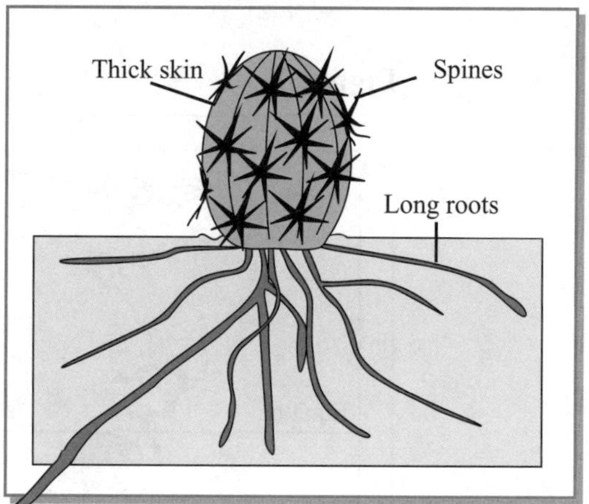

(a)   Use **Figure 2** to describe two ways in which plants can adapt to a hot desert climate.

1 ....

....

2 ....

....

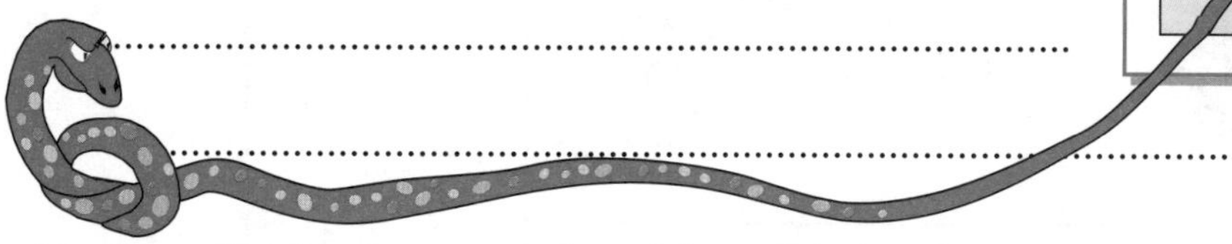

....

(2 marks)

(b)   Describe the characteristics of the soil in hot deserts.

....

....

(2 marks)

3   Study **Figure 3**, which shows climate data for a hot desert.

This is a complicated figure so read it carefully before you start the question.

Figure 3

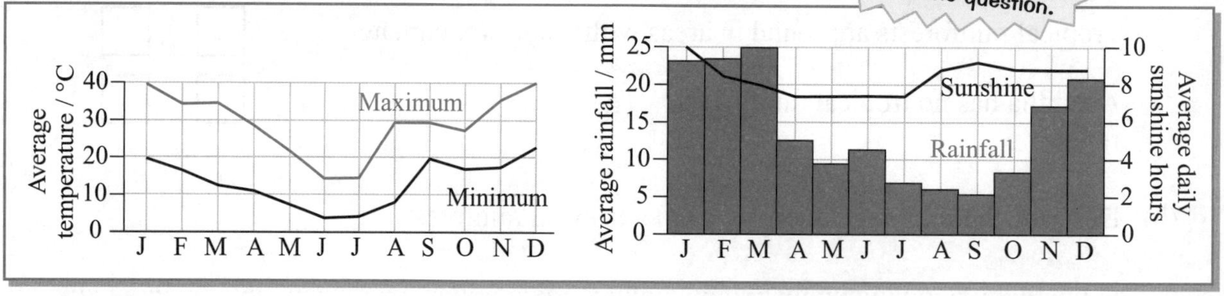

(a)   (i)   Which month has the highest average rainfall?

....

(1 mark)

(ii)   What is the average maximum temperature for December?

....°C

(1 mark)

(b)   Use **Figure 3** to describe the pattern of sunshine and rainfall in the hot desert climate.

Sunshine ....

....

Rainfall ....

....

(4 marks)

World Ecosystems

4   Study **Figure 4**, which shows climate data for an area of temperate deciduous forest.

(a) (i) Which month has the highest
average temperature?

....
(1 mark)

(ii) Use **Figure 4** to describe the
pattern of temperature and rainfall
in this temperate deciduous forest.

Temperature ....

....

....

Rainfall ....

....

....
(2 marks)

Figure 4

Month	Average temperature / °C	Average rainfall / mm
January	2	64
February	5	42
March	6	33
April	12	42
May	19	45
June	19	48
July	21	69
August	19	62
September	12	45
October	10	55
November	4	65
December	2	52

(b) Tick the correct box to show whether
each of the following statements about
temperate deciduous forests is **True** or **False**.

                                                True   **False**

Temperate deciduous forests are only found south of the equator. ☐ ☐

They are found in most of Europe, south east USA, China and Japan. ☐ ☐

They are found in places where there are four distinct seasons. ☐ ☐

Temperate deciduous forests have four layers of vegetation. ☐ ☐
(4 marks)

(c) (i) Describe the vegetation structure of a deciduous forest.

....

....

....
(3 marks)

(ii) Explain one way that plants are adapted to life in a temperate deciduous forest.

....
(1 mark)

(d) Give two characteristics of the soil in a temperate deciduous forest.

....
(2 marks)

Temperate Deciduous Forest

1 Study **Figure 1**, a bar chart showing how visitors use a temperate deciduous forest.

Figure 1

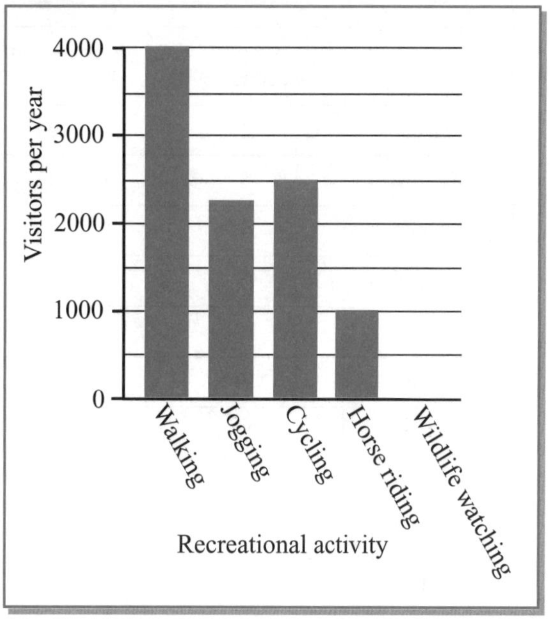

(a) (i) How many visitors use the forest for jogging each year?

....
(1 mark)

(ii) Complete the bar chart to show that 2750 visitors use the forest for wildlife watching each year.
(1 mark)

(iii) How many people in total use the forest each year?

....

....
(1 mark)

You'll need to use your calculator for this one.

(iv) What percentage of visitors use the forest for horse riding?

....
(1 mark)

(b) Suggest two other uses of temperate deciduous forests that aren't shown in **Figure 1**.

1 ....

2 ....
(2 marks)

(c) Suggest how the activities in **Figure 1** could have a negative impact on the forest.

....

....

....

....
(4 marks)

(d) Replanting new trees after trees have been cut down is a management strategy used in forests. Explain why this is a sustainable strategy.

....
(1 mark)

2 Describe the strategies used to manage a temperate deciduous forest you have studied.

(6 marks)

Tropical Rainforest — Deforestation

1   Study **Figure 1**, a series of maps showing the extent of deforestation in an area of tropical rainforest between 1958 and 2008.

Figure 1

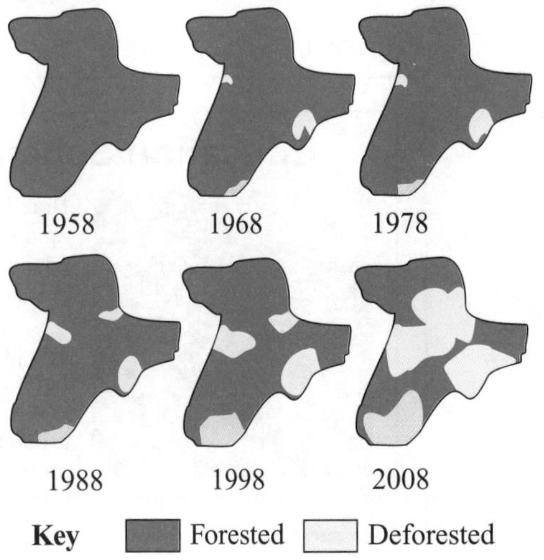

1958	1968	1978
1988	1998	2008

Key   ■ Forested   □ Deforested

(a)   Tick the correct box to show whether each of the following statements about the deforestation of the tropical rainforest in **Figure 1** is **True** or **False**.

	True	False
Deforestation started after 1958.	☐	☐
Two new areas of deforestation appeared in 1988.	☐	☐
All deforested areas decreased in size between 1968 and 2008.	☐	☐

(3 marks)

(b)   (i)   Complete the paragraph below, which describes two causes of deforestation. Choose the correct words from the following list.

slash and burn	ecotourism	slash and bury	subsistence farms
habitats	sheep farms	access routes	mineral extraction

Rainforest can be cleared to set up small .... or large commercial

cattle ranches. Often the "................................." technique is used to clear the forest.

Another cause of deforestation is .... Trees are cut down to expose

ground and clear ....

(3 marks)

(ii)   Describe one other cause of rainforest deforestation.

....

....

(2 marks)

(c)   Give one advantage of deforestation.

....

(1 mark)

(d)   Describe the environmental impacts of rainforest deforestation.

Always reread long answers to check your answer makes sense and it's all spelt correctly.

....

....

....

....

(4 marks)

Unit 1A — The Living World

Tropical Rainforest — Sustainable Management

1   Study **Figure 1**, part of a newspaper article on the Amazon Education Project in Brazil.

Figure 1

Education Scheme Offers Hope for Amazon Rainforest

Brazilian environmentalists have set up an Education Project that aims to educate the local population about the devastating impacts of deforestation.

The project manager Silverado Arboles said: "The local population is reliant on the rainforest, but the problem is that they can make a lot of money from illegal logging.

Hardwoods such as mahogany fetch high prices so it is hard to find alternative sources of income that pay as much".

The project also aims to help locals to sustainably manage the forest — it runs schemes to teach locals selective logging techniques, and it provides discounted tree saplings for replanting schemes.

(a)   What is meant by 'the sustainable management of tropical rainforests'?

....

....

(2 marks)

(b)   (i)   Use evidence from **Figure 1** to give one way that forests can be sustainably managed.

....

(1 mark)

(ii)   Explain why the management strategy you have given in (b) (i) is sustainable.

....

....

....

(1 mark)

(c)   Some richer countries have increased taxes on imported mahogany to make it more expensive.
Suggest how this could help reduce deforestation.

....

....

(2 marks)

(d)   Some local people might not know about the environmental impacts of deforestation.
How can education projects help towards the sustainable management of tropical rainforests?

....

Felling = bad
Hugging = good   ....

....

....

(3 marks)

Tropical Rainforest — Sustainable Management

2   Study **Figure 2**, a graph showing the number of tourists visiting an area of tropical rainforest.

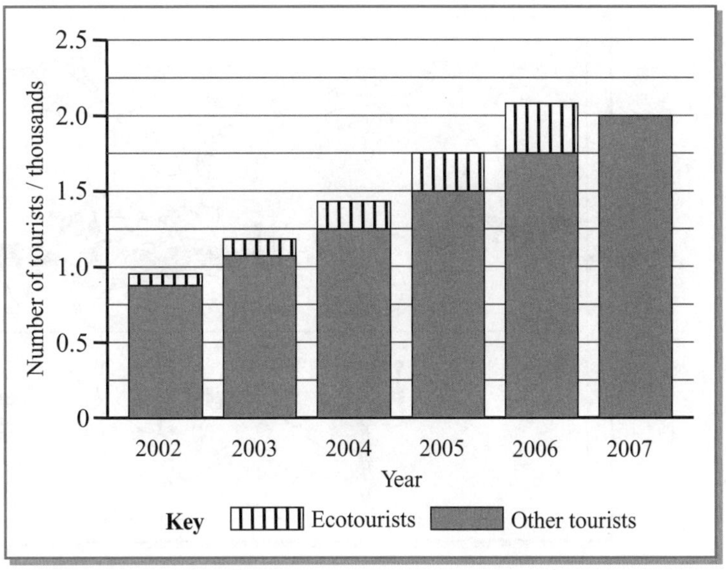

(a) (i)   How many tourists in total visited the area in 2005?

....
(1 mark)

> Always read the axis labels on graphs carefully so you are sure what's being measured and what the units are.

Figure 2

Key: Ecotourists | Other tourists

(ii)   Complete **Figure 2** to show that 400 ecotourists visited in 2007.
(1 mark)

(b) (i)   What is ecotourism?

....
(1 mark)

(ii)   Complete the paragraph below to explain how ecotourism can be part of a sustainable rainforest management strategy. Choose the correct words from the following list.

available	more	income	large
happiness	small	fewer	damaged

Ecotourism provides a source of .... for local people so they don't have to log or

farm to make money. This means .... trees are cut down, so there will be more

left for the future. Ecotourism is .... scale and aims to have as little impact on

the environment as possible. This means that the environment is not .... for

people in the future.

(4 marks)

(c)   Many rainforests are in poorer countries. Explain how reducing a country's debt can help to reduce deforestation.

....

....

....

....
(4 marks)

3   For a tropical rainforest you have studied, describe the strategies being used to reduce deforestation.

(6 marks)

Hot Deserts

1   Study **Figure 1**, which shows the global distribution of hot deserts and some of their main uses.

Figure 1

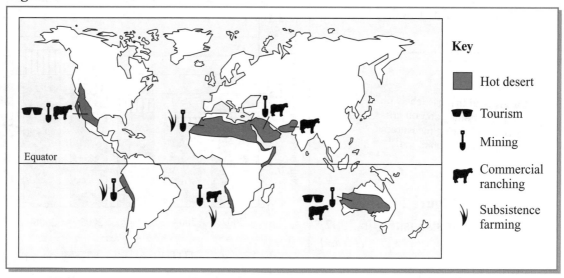

(a) (i)   Using **Figure 1**, describe the main uses of hot deserts in North America.

....
(1 mark)

(ii)   Use evidence from **Figure 1** to describe the
main uses of hot deserts in poor countries.

When answering questions like this try to use names of countries and regions in your answer.

....

....

....
(2 marks)

(b) People are moving to hot deserts because improvements in irrigation techniques are making
farming easier. Suggest one other reason why the population of a hot desert might increase.

....

....
(2 marks)

(c) Describe three negative impacts of the uses of hot deserts.

1 ....

2 ....

3 ....
(3 marks)

2   For a named hot desert, describe how management strategies
are used to ensure sustainable use of the area.

(6 marks)

The River Valley

1 Study **Figure 1**, which shows the long profile of a river.

(a) Complete **Figure 1** by labelling the source and mouth of the river.

(1 mark)

Figure 1

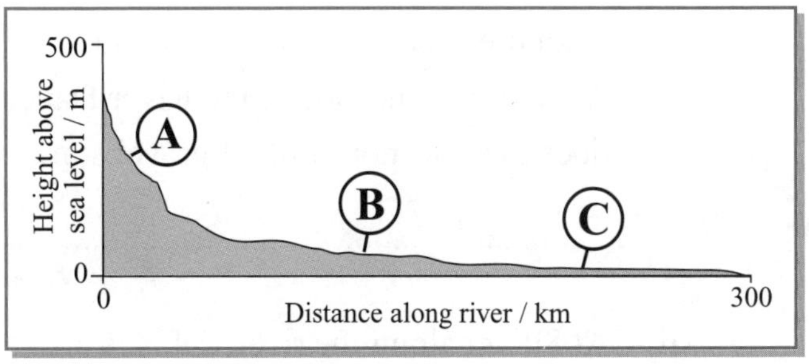

(b) (i) What is the difference between the long profile and the cross profile of a river?

....

....

....

(2 marks)

(ii) Circle the correct letter to show whether the description given below matches the cross profile at point A or point B in **Figure 1**.

A V-shaped valley with steep sides and a narrow, shallow channel.

A   **B**

(1 mark)

(iii) Draw a labelled sketch showing the cross profile that you would expect at the point labelled C in **Figure 1**.

Use a pencil to draw diagrams, then you can rub out any mistakes.

(3 marks)

(c) Complete the paragraph below to explain why the upper course of a river valley has a different cross profile from the lower course. Choose the correct words from this list.

lower   V-shaped   horizontal   deeper   wider   lateral   shallow   vertical

In the upper course of a river valley, ... erosion is dominant. This makes the valley

.... than in the lower course. In the lower course of a river valley, ...

erosion is dominant. This makes the valley .... than in the upper course.

(4 marks)

Erosion, Transportation and Deposition

1   Study **Figure 1**, which shows how the velocity of the River Dance varies along its course.

(a) (i)   Small gravel particles are transported by velocities above 0.1 m per second. At what distance along the River Dance does the transportation of gravel start?

Figure 1

....
(1 mark)

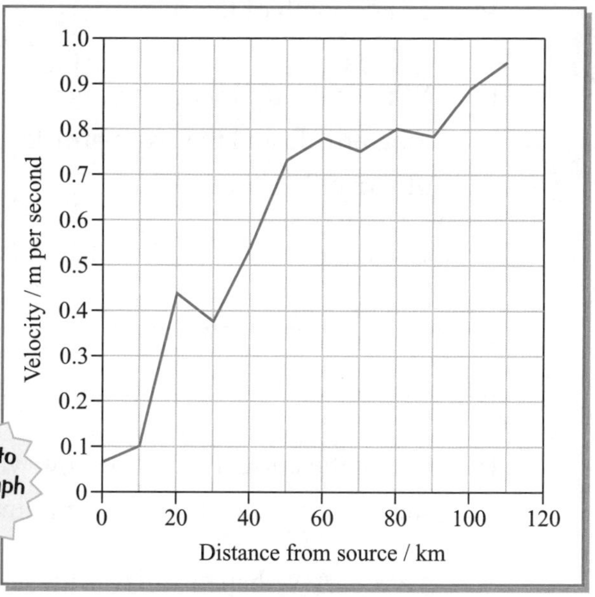

(ii) At 80 km along the river, pebbles are being transported. Give the velocity of the river at this point and name the process by which pebbles are transported.

Velocity ....

Use a ruler to read off a graph accurately.

Process ....

....
(2 marks)

(iii) Name and describe two other processes by which material is transported in rivers.

Process 1 ....

....

Process 2 ....

....
(4 marks)

(b) (i)   Name two processes of erosion that may take place in the River Dance.

....
(2 marks)

(ii) Describe the two processes you named in (b) (i).

....

....

....

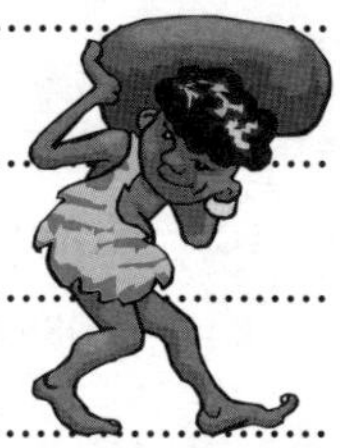

....
(2 marks)

(c)   Deposition occurs when rivers slow down. Describe two reasons why rivers slow down.

1 ....

2 ....
(2 marks)

River Landforms

1   Study **Figure 1**, which is a labelled photograph of a meander.

Figure 1

(a)   (i)   Suggest a feature likely to be found at the part of the river labelled A in **Figure 1**.

....

(1 mark)

(ii)   Tick the correct box to show whether each of the following statements about meanders is **True** or **False**.

	True	False
The current is faster on the outside of the bend.	☐	☐
Most erosion takes place on the inside of the bend.	☐	☐
The water is deepest on the inside of the bend.	☐	☐

(3 marks)

(iii)   Label a slip-off slope and the neck of a meander on **Figure 1**.

(2 marks)

(iv)   Complete the paragraph below to explain the formation of slip-off slopes. Choose the correct words from the following list.

deeper   faster   deposited   slower   eroded   shallower

The current is .... on the inside bend of the meander because the river channel

is .... This means material is .... on the inside of the bend,

so a slip-off slope is formed.

(3 marks)

(b)   Erosion causes the outside bends of meanders to get closer until there's only a small bit of land left between the bends. Explain how this can lead to the formation of an ox-bow lake.

Remember to check your answers through — you get marks for good spelling and grammar.

....

....

....

....

....

(4 marks)

River Landforms

2   Study **Figure 2**, which is an Ordnance Survey® map showing part of Snowdonia, Wales.

Figure 2

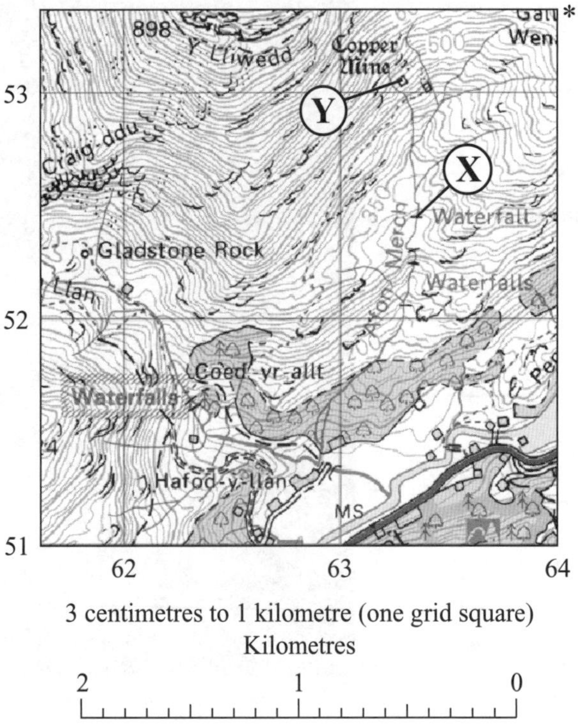

3 centimetres to 1 kilometre (one grid square)
Kilometres

(a) (i) Is the Afon Merch, shown in **Figure 2**, an upper course stream or a lower course stream?

....
(1 mark)

(ii) Use evidence from **Figure 2** to explain your answer to (a) (i).

....

....

....

....

....

....

....
(3 marks)

> Study the map carefully — you need to find at least three pieces of evidence.

(b) (i) A waterfall is found at point X on **Figure 2**.
Give the six figure grid reference for the waterfall.

....
(1 mark)

(ii) A copper mine is found at point Y on **Figure 2**.
State the distance in kilometres between the mine and the waterfall.

....
(1 mark)

(c) (i) Rivers sometimes flow over an area of hard rock followed by an area of softer rock.
Describe how this can result in the formation of waterfalls.

> Try to write about the stages in the order they occur — this will give your answer a logical structure.

....

....

....

....
(3 marks)

(ii) Name the landform that is left as a waterfall retreats.

....
(1 mark)

Unit 1B — Water on the Land

River Landforms

3   Study **Figure 3**, which shows a photograph of a river valley.

(a) (i)   Label **Figure 3** to show
           the flood plain of the river.
                                        (1 mark)

Figure 3

©iStockphoto.com

(ii)   What is a flood plain?

....

....
                                        (1 mark)

(iii) Complete the paragraph below to
       explain the formation of flood plains.
       Choose the correct words from this list.

speeds up   weathering   transporting   slows down   eroding   deposition

When a river floods onto a flood plain the water .... and deposits the eroded

material it's .... , which builds up the flood plain. Flood plains are also built

up by the .... that happens on the slip-off slopes of meanders.
                                                                        (3 marks)

(b) (i)   What are levees?

....

....
                                                                        (1 mark)

(ii)   Explain how levees form.

....

....

....
                                                                        (2 marks)

(iii) **Figure 4** is a cross profile diagram
       of point A shown on **Figure 3**.
       Draw a labelled sketch showing
       the levees that could form at this point.

Figure 4

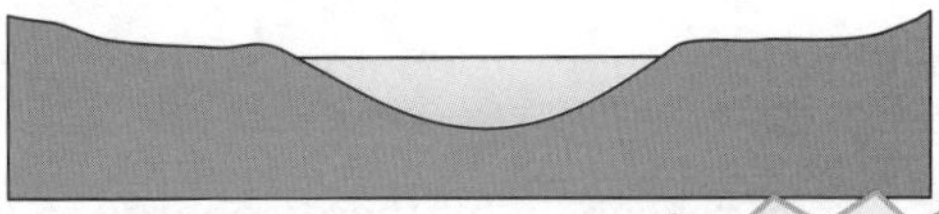

Your sketch doesn't need to be a beautiful drawing — the main thing is to show the levees clearly.

                                                                        (2 marks)

River Discharge

1   Study **Figure 1**, which shows storm hydrographs for two rivers.

Figure 1

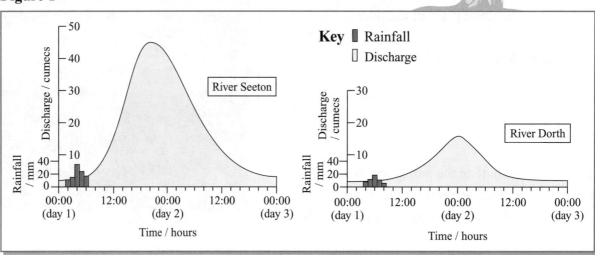

(a) (i)   Explain what the following terms mean:

Peak discharge ....

Lag time ....
(2 marks)

(ii)   At what time was the River Seeton at peak discharge? ....
(1 mark)

(iii) Peak rainfall around the River Dorth was at 06:00 on day 1. What was the lag time?

....
(1 mark)

(b) Contrast the peak discharge and lag time for the two storm hydrographs shown in **Figure 1**.

Peak discharge ....

....

Lag time ....

....
(2 marks)

> 'Contrast' means talk about the differences.

(c) Suggest reasons why the discharge is different for the storm hydrographs shown in **Figure 1**.

....

....

....

....

....
(4 marks)

> Use info from the figure as well as your own knowledge to answer a question like this.

Flooding

1   Study **Figure 1** and **Figure 2**, which show the frequency of flooding
of the River Turb and a recent article from a local newspaper.

Figure 1

Year	1997 – 1998	1998 – 1999	1999 – 2000	2000 – 2001	2001 – 2002	2002 – 2003	2003 – 2004	2004 – 2005	2005 – 2006	2006 – 2007	2007 – 2008
Number of floods	0	1	1	0	0	2	2	3	2	4	3

Figure 2

RAIN, RAIN, GO AWAY...

Downpours to continue

For the second week in a row
there's only one thing in the
weather forecast — rain, and
lots of it. Despite promises of sunshine, heavy rainfall
is expected to hit most places around the county again.
Many people are worried that the River Turb, which
runs through Sopping, will flood for the second time
this year. Scientists have warned that higher than
normal snowmelt could make these fears come true.

(a) (i) Using **Figure 1**, circle the answer that
most accurately describes the trend in
frequency of flooding.

Frequency of flooding decreased
between 1997 and 2008.

Frequency of flooding increased
between 1997 and 2008.

Frequency of flooding remained
constant between 1997 and 2008.

(1 mark)

(ii) Using **Figure 2**, explain two physical factors that may cause the River Turb to flood.

1 ....

....

2 ....

....

(4 marks)

(iii) State one other physical factor that would make the River Turb likely to flood.

....

(1 mark)

(b) Explain one human factor that can increase the risk of flooding.

....

....

....

....

(2 marks)

(c) Compare the primary and secondary effects of flooding
in rich and poor parts of the world that you have studied.

'Compare'
means talk about
the similarities
and differences.

(6 marks)

Hard vs Soft Engineering

1   Study **Figure 1**, which shows some of the engineering strategies used to combat flooding along the River Joiner.

Figure 1

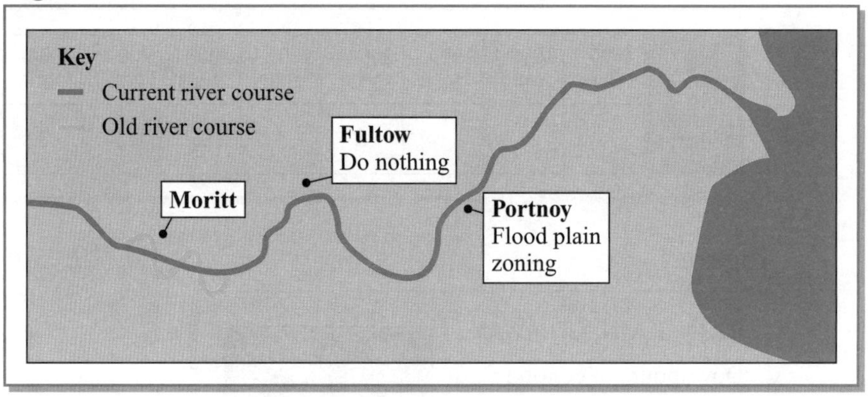

(a) Hard engineering strategies use man-made structures to control the flow of rivers.
What are soft engineering strategies?

....

....

Key
— Current river course
Old river course

Fultow
Do nothing

Moritt

Portnoy
Flood plain zoning

....

....

(1 mark)

(b) (i)   What engineering strategy has been used to protect Moritt?

....

(1 mark)

(ii) Describe the engineering strategy being used at Portnoy and its benefits.

....

....

....

....

(3 marks)

Figure 2

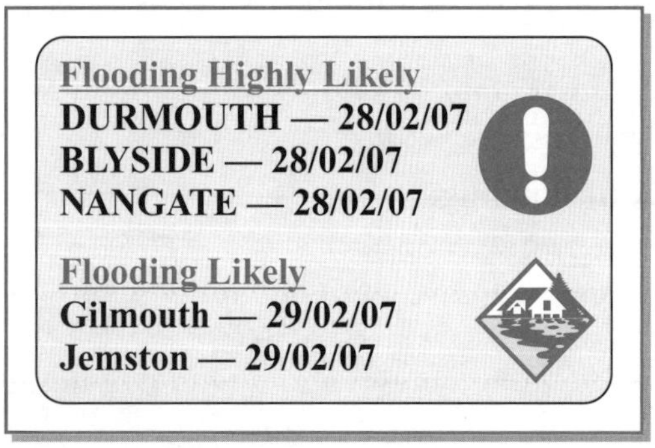

Flooding Highly Likely
DURMOUTH — 28/02/07
BLYSIDE — 28/02/07
NANGATE — 28/02/07

Flooding Likely
Gilmouth — 29/02/07
Jemston — 29/02/07

(c) (i)   Study **Figure 2**, which shows an extract from a web page. What type of strategy does **Figure 2** show?

....

(1 mark)

(ii) Describe two disadvantages of the type of strategy shown in **Figure 2**.

Disadvantages are sometimes called costs.

....

....

....

....

(2 marks)

Managing the UK's Water

1   Study **Figure 1** and **Figure 2**, which show rainfall and population density in the UK.

(a) (i)   Tick the correct box to show whether each of the following statements is **True** or **False**.

Figure 1

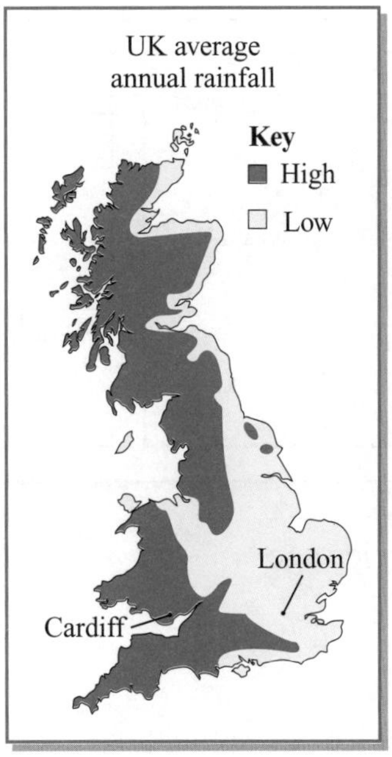

UK average annual rainfall

Key
■ High
□ Low

London

Cardiff

Figure 2

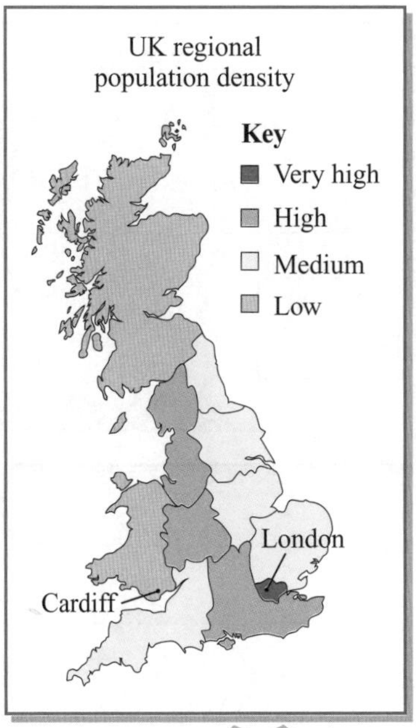

UK regional population density

Key
■ Very high
■ High
□ Medium
■ Low

London

Cardiff

               True   **False**

The north and west of the UK have high rainfall. ☐ ☐

The south east of the UK has a low population density. ☐ ☐

A low population density means there is a high demand for water. ☐ ☐

(3 marks)

(ii)   Explain why Cardiff has a water surplus and London has a water deficit.

'Explain' means you need to give the reasons why.

Cardiff ....

....

London ....

....

(2 marks)

(b) (i)   The supply of water can be managed by transferring water from areas of surplus to areas of deficit. Describe two issues that this strategy could cause.

....

....

(2 marks)

(ii)   Give two other ways in which the supply of water in the UK can be managed.

....

....

(2 marks)

(c)   Describe one way that the demand for water in the UK can be reduced.

....

(1 mark)

2   Describe the economic, social and environmental impacts of a reservoir you have studied.

(6 marks)

Unit 1B — Ice on the Land

Ice Levels Over Time

1   Study **Figure 1**, which shows the extent of global ice coverage 20 000 years ago and today.

Figure 1

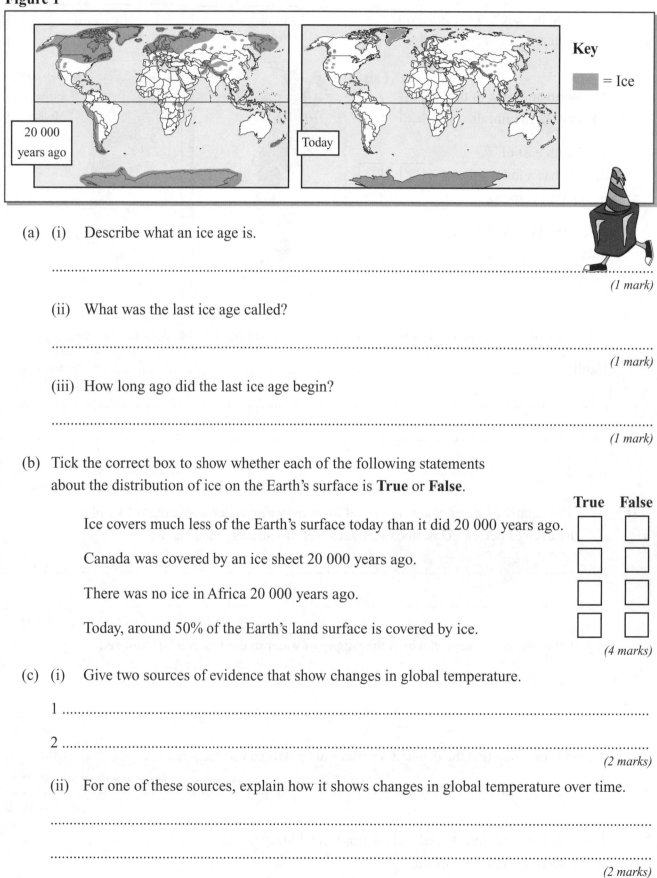

(a) (i)   Describe what an ice age is.

....
(1 mark)

(ii)   What was the last ice age called?

....
(1 mark)

(iii) How long ago did the last ice age begin?

....
(1 mark)

(b) Tick the correct box to show whether each of the following statements
about the distribution of ice on the Earth's surface is **True** or **False**.

	True	**False**
Ice covers much less of the Earth's surface today than it did 20 000 years ago.	☐	☐
Canada was covered by an ice sheet 20 000 years ago.	☐	☐
There was no ice in Africa 20 000 years ago.	☐	☐
Today, around 50% of the Earth's land surface is covered by ice.	☐	☐

(4 marks)

(c) (i)   Give two sources of evidence that show changes in global temperature.

1 ....

2 ....
(2 marks)

(ii)   For one of these sources, explain how it shows changes in global temperature over time.

....

....
(2 marks)

Glacial Budget

1   Study **Figure 1**, a graph showing how the length of a glacier changed between 1900 and 2000.

(a)   (i)   What is meant by the term 'ablation'?

Figure 1

....

....

(1 mark)

(ii)   On which part of a glacier does most ablation occur?

....

(1 mark)

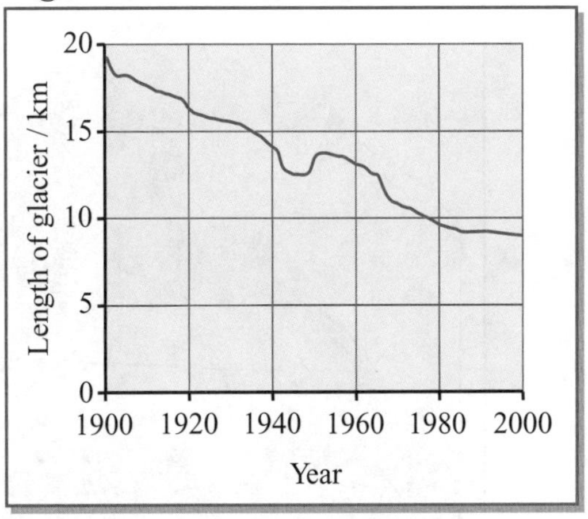

(b)   (i)   Draw a line to link each of the statements below to complete the sentences about glacial budgets.

The glacial budget is	when ablation exceeds accumulation.
A positive glacial budget is	when there is the same amount of accumulation and ablation over one year.
A negative glacial budget is	when accumulation exceeds ablation.
The glacier stays the same size	the difference between total accumulation and total ablation for one year.

(3 marks)

(ii)   What type of glacial budget does the glacier shown in **Figure 1** have?

....

(1 mark)

(iii)   By how much did the glacier shown in **Figure 1** change in length between 1900 and 2000?

....

(1 mark)

(c)   (i)   How you would expect the length of a glacier to change during winter?

....

(1 mark)

(ii)   Explain your answer to (i).

....

....

(2 marks)

2   For a retreating glacier you have studied, describe the causes of retreat and the evidence for it.

Remember to put in lots of juicy details when writing about a case study.

(6 marks)

Glacial Erosion

1 Study **Figure 1**, a diagram of a mountainous area where glaciers used to flow.

Figure 1

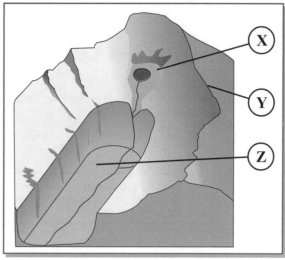

(a) (i) Name the glacial landforms labelled X, Y and Z on **Figure 1**.

X ....

Y ....

Z ....

(3 marks)

(ii) Describe how moving ice erodes the landscape by plucking and abrasion.

Plucking ....

....

....

Abrasion ....

....

(2 marks)

(b) Complete the paragraph below to explain how the rock above glaciers is broken down by weathering. Choose the correct words from this list.

wetting-drying   **thaws**   **erodes**   **expands**   **freeze-thaw**   **heats**

Rock above glaciers is weathered by a process called .... weathering. Water gets into

cracks in rocks and freezes and .... , putting pressure on the rock. It then .... ,

releasing the pressure. If this process is repeated it can make bits of the rock fall off.

(3 marks)

(c) Study **Figure 2**, a photograph of an Alpine landscape.

(i) Name the glacial landform labelled A in **Figure 2**.

....

(1 mark)

(ii) Explain how this landform is formed.

....

....

....

....

Figure 2

©iStockphoto.com/ Peter Wey

Always double check you've named the right thing in a labelled photograph.

(3 marks)

Glacial Erosion

2   Study **Figure 3**, an Ordnance Survey® map of part of the Lake District.

Figure 3

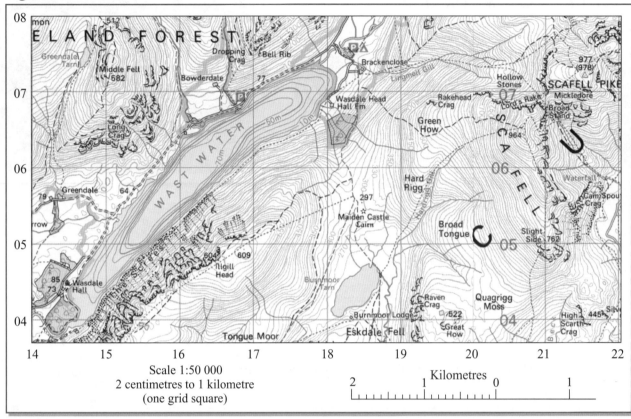

Scale 1:50 000
2 centimetres to 1 kilometre
(one grid square)

(a)   There is a truncated spur at grid reference 152065. How are truncated spurs formed?

....
(1 mark)

(b) (i)   Name the type of glacial landform found between grid references 146040 and 181072.

....
(1 mark)

   (ii)   How long is this glacial landform? .... km

(1 mark)

  (iii)   Describe this type of landform and explain how it is formed.

Mark the grid references with a cross on the map to help you.

....

....
(2 marks)

(c) (i)   Give the six-figure grid reference for a pyramidal peak shown in **Figure 3**.

....
(1 mark)

   (ii)   Describe how pyramidal peaks are formed.

....
(1 mark)

* *Map: Reproduced from Ordnance Survey*
digital map data © Crown copyright 2001

Glacial Transport and Deposition

1   Study **Figure 1**, a photograph of a glacier.

Figure 1

(a) (i)   What is meant by the term 'bulldozing'?

....

....
(1 mark)

(ii)   Glaciers deposit material when the ice is overloaded. Give one other way that glaciers deposit material.

....
(1 mark)

(b) (i)   Name the two types of moraine labelled A and B on **Figure 1**.

A ....

B ....
(2 marks)

(ii)   Explain the formation of these two types of moraine.

....

....
(2 marks)

> There's only one mark for each explanation, so your answer doesn't need to be too long.

(iii) Name one other type of moraine.

....
(1 mark)

(c) **Figure 2** is a sketch map of a drumlin.

Figure 2

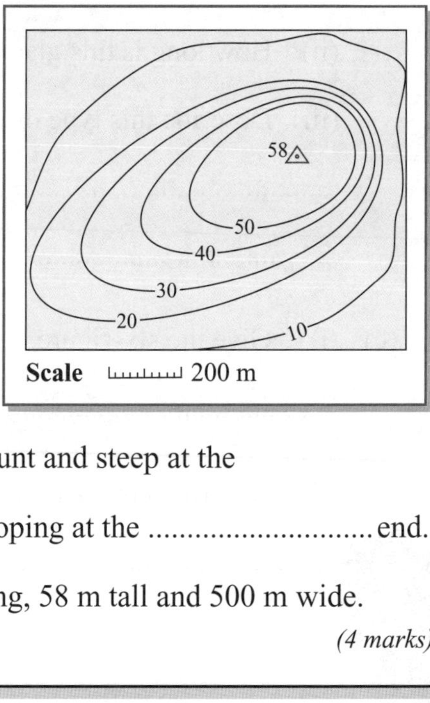

Scale └──────┘ 200 m

(i)   Label the sketch map to show the direction of ice flow.
(1 mark)

(ii)   Complete the paragraph below to describe the characteristics of a drumlin. Choose the correct words from this list.

spherical	**600**	**upstream**	**elongated**
downstream	**1000**	**lateral**	**pyramidal**

Drumlins are .... hills which are round, blunt and steep at the

.... end and tapered, pointed and gently sloping at the .... end.

The drumlin in Figure 2 is about .... m long, 58 m tall and 500 m wide.
(4 marks)

Impacts and Management of Tourism on Ice

1   Study **Figure 1**, a photograph of a ski resort.

Figure 1

(a) (i)   Using **Figure 1**, describe one economic
            and one environmental impact
            of tourism on the surrounding area.

Economic ....

....

Environmental ....

....
(2 marks)

     (ii)   Tourists can trigger avalanches on ski slopes, which can cause injuries and deaths.
            Explain two other social impacts of tourism in areas covered in snow and ice.

1 ....

....

2 ....

....
(2 marks)

(b) Complete the paragraph below to describe the strategies used to manage the impacts
     of tourism in areas covered in snow and ice. Choose the correct words from this list.

pedestrians	**glaciers**	**reduced**
increased	**traffic**	**avalanches**

Resorts can reduce the impacts of .... by building structures to slow and divert

moving snow, and planting trees to act as barriers.

Improvements to public transport systems can reduce the amount of .... and so

reduce damage to the environment from pollution.

Areas can be set aside as nature reserves. Tourist activity in these areas is limited, so their

environmental impact is ....
(3 marks)

(c) For an Alpine area you have studied, describe the attractions for tourists
     and the impacts tourists have on the area.
(6 marks)

2   For an Alpine area you have studied, describe the strategies
     used to manage tourism in the area. 
(6 marks)

Impacts of Glacial Retreat

1   Study **Figure 1**, a graph showing annual snowfall and unemployment between 1999 and 2008 in an area covered in snow and ice.

Figure 1

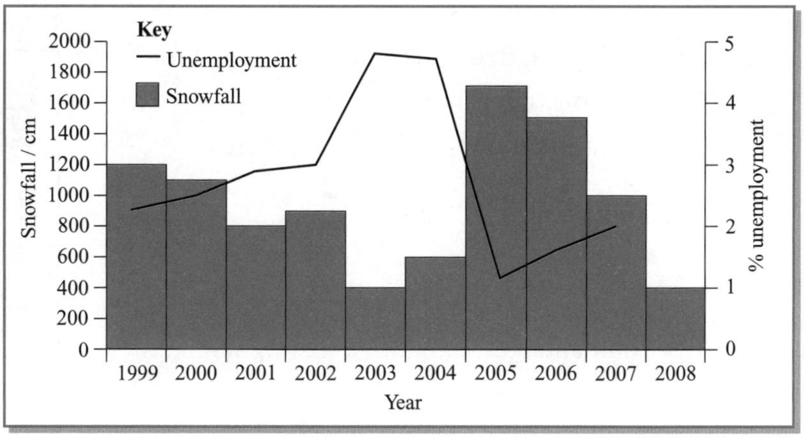

(a) (i)   Complete the graph to show that unemployment was 4.5% in 2008.

(1 mark)

Take care to make your line precise — use a ruler and a sharp pencil.

(ii)   How much snowfall was there in 2002?

....
(1 mark)

(b)   Tick the correct box to show whether each of the following statements about snowfall and unemployment is **True** or **False**.

	True	False
Between 2003 and 2008, snowfall first decreased then increased.	☐	☐
Percentage unemployment was highest in 2003.	☐	☐
Percentage unemployment decreased from 2000 to 2003.	☐	☐
As snowfall decreases, unemployment increases.	☐	☐

(4 marks)

(c)   Glacial retreat means the ice will no longer be available for winter sports or sightseeing, so the area will attract fewer tourists. Explain how this will affect unemployment in glacial areas.

....

....
(2 marks)

(d)   Describe one social and one environmental impact of unreliable snowfall and glacial retreat.

Social ....

....

....

Environmental ....

....

....
(4 marks)

Unit 1B — Ice on the Land

Coastal Weathering and Erosion

1 Study **Figure 1**, which shows how the coastline of an area has changed over time.

Figure 1

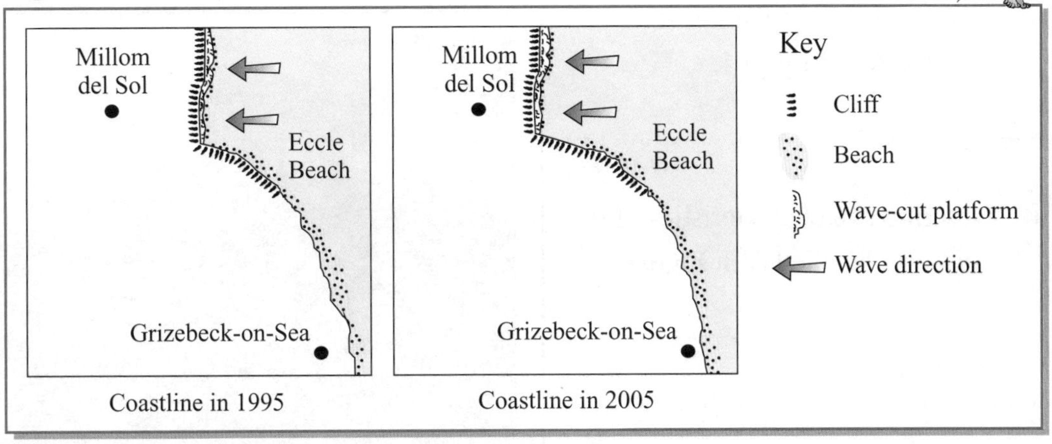
Millom del Sol
Eccle Beach
Grizebeck-on-Sea
Millom del Sol
Eccle Beach
Grizebeck-on-Sea
Key
Cliff
Beach
Wave-cut platform
Wave direction

Coastline in 1995 Coastline in 2005

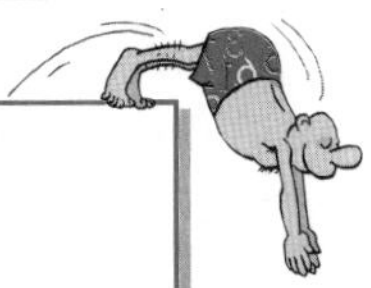

(a) (i) Are the waves shown in **Figure 1** constructive waves or destructive waves?

....

(1 mark)

(ii) Tick the correct box to show whether each of the following statements is **True** or **False**.

	True	**False**
Constructive waves have a higher frequency than destructive waves.	☐	☐
Destructive waves are steeper than constructive waves.	☐	☐
Destructive waves have a more powerful backwash than swash.	☐	☐

(3 marks)

(b) Name and describe one process of erosion that acts on coastlines.

....

....

(2 marks)

(c) Complete the paragraph below to explain how freeze-thaw weathering causes rock on coastal cliffs to break up. Choose the correct words from this list.

Cross out words that you've used to make sure you don't use them again.

contracts	**water**	**ice**	**break**
cracks	**expands**	**clog**	**freeze**

Freeze-thaw weathering can happen when .... gets into rock that has cracks. If the water freezes it ...., which puts pressure on the rock. If the water then thaws it ...., which releases the pressure on the rock. Repeated freezing and thawing widens the cracks and causes the rock to .... up.

(4 marks)

(d) Name one type of mass movement that acts on coastlines.

....

(1 mark)

Coastal Landforms Caused by Erosion

1   Study **Figure 1**, a photograph showing coastal landforms.

(a) (i) Name the type of landform labelled A in **Figure 1**.

....
(1 mark)

Figure 1

(ii) Describe two characteristics of the landform labelled A in **Figure 1**.

....

....

....

....
(2 marks)

(iii) Explain why the landforms shown in **Figure 1** form in areas where there are alternating bands of resistant and less resistant rock.

....

....
(2 marks)

(b) Study **Figure 2**, which shows one step in the formation of a wave-cut platform.

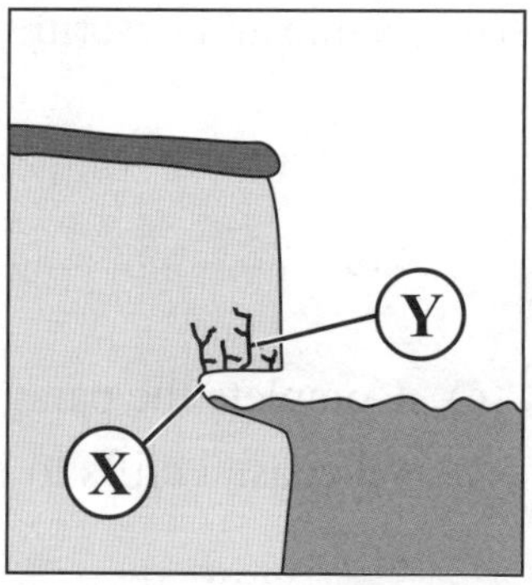

(i) Name the features indicated by labels X and Y.

X: ....

Y: ....
(2 marks)

Figure 2

(ii) Complete the paragraph below to explain the formation of wave-cut platforms. Choose the correct words from this list.

| head | stable | unstable | washed |
| collapsing | melted | crushing | foot |

Waves cause most erosion at the .... of a cliff. This forms a wave-cut notch, which is enlarged as erosion continues. The rock above the notch becomes .... and eventually collapses. The collapsed material is .... away and a new wave-cut notch starts to form. Repeated .... results in the cliff retreating.

A wave-cut platform is the platform that's left behind as the cliff retreats.
(4 marks)

Coastal Landforms Caused by Erosion

2   Study **Figure 3**, a photograph of a coastal area.

Figure 3

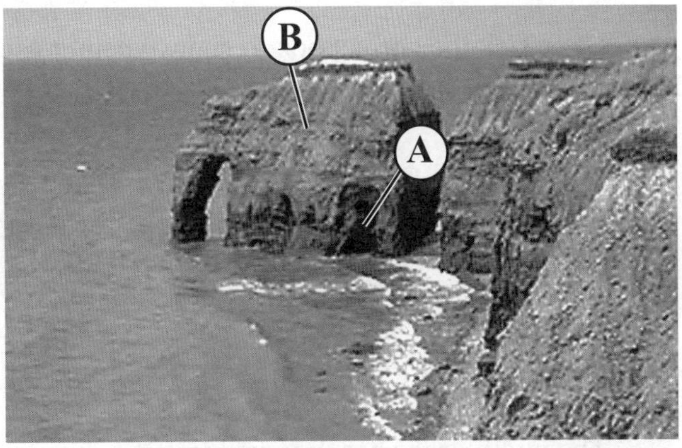

(a) (i) Name the type of landform labelled A in **Figure 3**.

....
(1 mark)

(ii) Explain how it might have formed from a crack in the rock.

....

....

....
(2 marks)

(b) (i) Label **Figure 3** to show an arch.
(1 mark)

(ii) Complete the paragraph below to explain how an arch is formed. Choose the correct words from this list.

within   deepens   rock   stack   from   smoothes

An arch forms .... a cave. Continued erosion .... the

cave until it breaks through the .... and forms an arch.
(3 marks)

(c) (i) Name the type of landform labelled B in **Figure 3**.

....
(1 mark)

(ii) Describe the characteristics of this landform.

....
(1 mark)

(d) Study **Figure 4**, a photograph of an arch and a cave. Suggest what might happen to the arch and the cave after continued erosion.

Figure 4

Arch ....

....

Cave ....

For this question you have to suggest the effects that continued erosion might have.

(2 marks)

©iStockphoto.com/Sylwia Kucharska

Coastal Transportation and Deposition

1   Study **Figure 1**, a graph showing how the width of a beach
    varied along its length in the years 2000 and 2005.

(a) (i)   Tick the correct box to show whether each
          of the following statements is **True** or **False**.

Figure 1

                                        True   False

At 0 m, the beach was wider   ☐   ☐
in 2000 than it was in 2005.

At 1000 m, the beach was wider   ☐   ☐
in 2000 than it was in 2005.

The width of the beach varied less   ☐   ☐
in 2000 than it did in 2005.

                                        (3 marks)

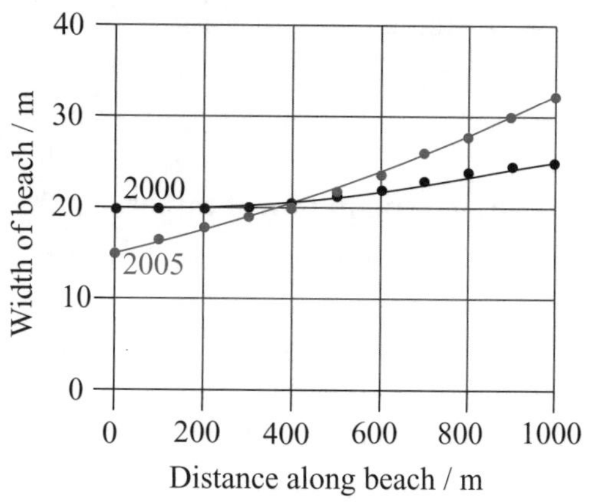

(ii) The changes in the width of the beach were caused by longshore drift.
      Describe the process of longshore drift.

Write your answer in a logical order, so each point follows on from the one before.

....

....

....

....

                                                                                        (4 marks)

(b) Name and describe two other processes of transportation that take place in the sea.

Process 1 ....

....

Process 2 ....

....

                                                                                        (4 marks)

(c) (i)   The total volume of material on the beach increased between 2000 and 2005 because
          large amounts of material, carried by sea water, were dropped on the coast.
          What is the name of this process?

....

                                                                                        (1 mark)

(ii) Suggest two factors that affect the amount of material dropped on the coast.

....

....

                                                                                        (2 marks)

Coastal Landforms Caused by Deposition

1   Study **Figure 1**, an Ordnance Survey® map of a coastal area near Bournemouth.

Figure 1

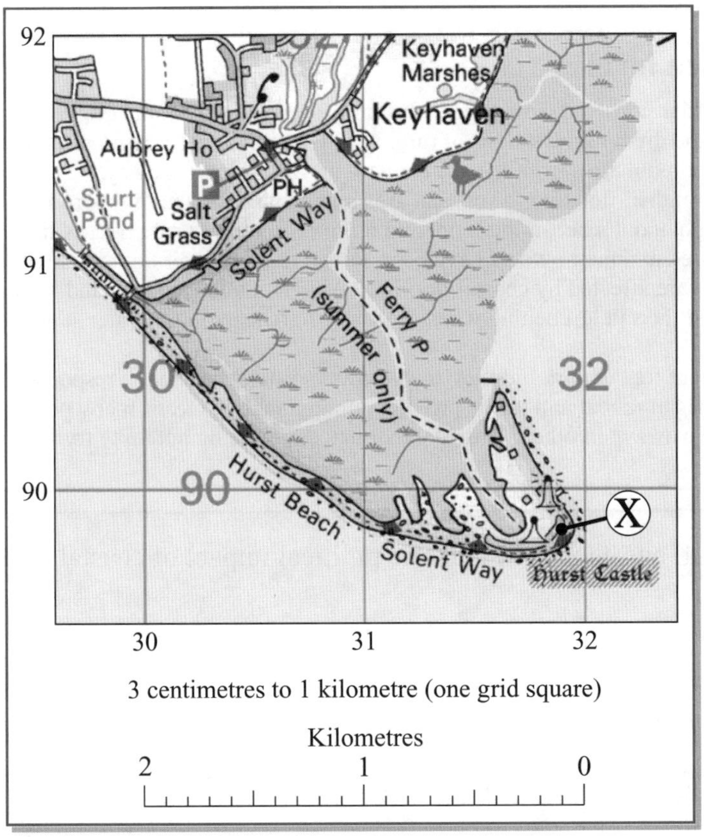

3 centimetres to 1 kilometre (one grid square)

Kilometres

2   1   0

(a) (i)   Hurst Castle is found at X
          on **Figure 1**. Give the
          six figure grid reference
          for Hurst Castle.

....
                                    (1 mark)

    (ii) State the distance between
          Hurst Castle and the end of
          the spit at 316905.

....
                                    (1 mark)

    *You'll need to use a
    ruler and the scale at
    the bottom of Figure 1
    to work this out.*

(b) Explain how a spit is formed.

....

....

....

....
                                    (2 marks)

(c) Tick the correct box to show whether each of the following characteristics applies to spits,
     to bars or to both types of landform.

	Spits	Bars	Both
Formed by longshore drift.	☐	☐	☐
Joined to the coast at one end only.	☐	☐	☐
May lead to the formation of a lagoon.	☐	☐	☐

                                    (3 marks)

Figure 2

(d) **Figure 2** is a picture of a sandy beach.

    (i)   Describe the characteristics of the beach
          shown in **Figure 2**.

....
                                    (1 mark)

    (ii) Name one other type of beach.

....
                                    (1 mark)

Rising Sea Level and Coastal Flooding

1   Study **Figure 1**, a news article about the effects of rising sea level on Australia.

Figure 1

The rising costs of rising sea level

The idea of living in a multi-million dollar house on the Sydney coast may seem like a dream lifestyle, but for many people living in the area the dream shows signs of turning into a nightmare. Rising sea level means that houses that used to be a hundred metres from the sea are now just a few metres away. In stormy weather the water rises even higher, flooding the coastal area and damaging many properties. The cost of repairing this damage is high and it's becoming more and more difficult to insure houses in the area. Some houses cannot be repaired and their owners have been forced to leave their homes and move elsewhere. And it's not just houses that are affected by coastal flooding. Vegetation is damaged and land is eroded by the influx of sea water, whilst the salt left behind when the water retreats pollutes water supplies and leaves farmland unusable.

Residents are turning to local government for support, but they're not always satisfied with the response. The policy in some areas is to allow coastal retreat and this is proving unpopular, as it means many people will have to leave their homes and move away. In other areas, flood defences are being put up to try and tackle the problems of rising sea level.

(a)   Using **Figure 1**, describe one social, one economic and one political impact of coastal flooding.

Social ....

....

Economic ....

Only write about the impacts mentioned in Figure 1.

....

Political ....

....

(3 marks)

(b)   Suggest two ways that coastal flooding can impact on the environment.

....

....

(2 marks)

(c)   Rising sea level is caused by global warming.
State two effects of global warming that cause sea level to rise.

1 ....

....

2 ....

....

(2 marks)

(d)   Describe the social and economic impacts of
coastal flooding on an area you have studied.

(6 marks)

Coastal Erosion

1   Study **Figure 1**, a sketch map
of the Sparkington coastal area.

Figure 1

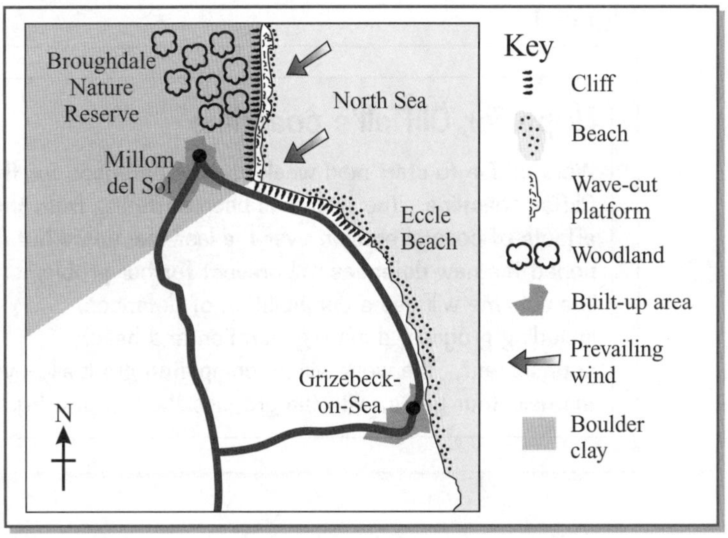

(a) (i) Which part of the Sparkington
coastline is being most
rapidly eroded, the northern
part or the southern part?

....
(1 mark)

(ii) Give two pieces of evidence
from **Figure 1** to explain your
answer to (a) (i).

1 ....

....

2 ....

....
(2 marks)

(b) Suggest how coastal erosion could affect the lives of people in Sparkington.

....

....

....

....
(4 marks)

Look for evidence on the map of anything that could be lost or damaged if the coast retreated.

(c) Give one potential environmental impact of coastal retreat in Sparkington.

....
(1 mark)

(d) Coastal defences, including groynes, are being built at Eccle Beach.
Explain why this might increase coastal erosion at Grizebeck-on-Sea.

....

....
(2 marks)

2   Describe the economic and environmental impacts of
coastal erosion on a coastal area you have studied.
(6 marks)

Coastal Management Strategies

1   Study **Figure 1**, a news article about coastal defences in Cliffall, a UK coastal town.

Figure 1

Hope for Cliffall's coastline

Work is due to start next week on new defences for the Cliffall coastline. The town has been suffering from the effects of coastal erosion over the last few years but it's hoped the new defences will prevent further problems. The scheme will use a combination of defences, including groynes, dune regeneration and beach nourishment. The work will be completed gradually over the next four years, with the groynes the top priority.

(a) (i)   What is meant by a 'soft engineering' coastal defence?

....
(1 mark)

(ii)   Name one soft engineering strategy mentioned in **Figure 1**.

....
(1 mark)

(b) (i)   Describe one benefit of a soft engineering strategy mentioned in **Figure 1**.

....
(1 mark)

(ii)   Describe two disadvantages of using this strategy as a method of coastal defence.

1 ....

2 ....
(2 marks)

(c) (i)   Name and describe one hard engineering strategy not mentioned in **Figure 1** that could be used to protect the coastline.

....

....
(2 marks)

(ii)   Explain two advantages of using this strategy as a coastal defence.

1 ....

2 ....
(2 marks)

(d) Explain the benefits of the coastal management strategies used in an area you have studied.
(6 marks)

Coastal Habitat

1   Study **Figure 1**, an article about mangrove forests.

Figure 1

Mangrove Forests

Mangrove forests are found on tropical and subtropical coasts, in areas where saline (salty) seawater mixes with freshwater from the land. Mangrove trees are adapted to this environment as they have roots that can filter salt out of water.
The forests are home to many species of birds, animals and fish. In fact, up to 75% of tropical fish use mangroves for food, shelter or breeding grounds.

Mangrove forests are also important to humans — providing protection from coastal erosion, flooding, and storm surges. Unfortunately, large areas of mangrove forest are at risk from human activities such as urban development, shrimp farming, pollution, over-fishing and deforestation. For example, the Indus Delta in Pakistan, which has 1600 square km of mangrove forest, provides wood for fuel and fishing grounds for over 100 000 people.

Conservation strategies have been implemented to limit the damage caused by these activities. Strategies include increasing the availability of alternatives to wood for fuel and limiting the mesh size of fishing nets, which prevents smaller fish being caught before they've had a chance to breed. It's hoped that these conservation strategies will help the forests survive well into the future.

(a) Using evidence from **Figure 1**, suggest why it is important to conserve mangrove forests.

....

....
(2 marks)

(b) (i)   Give one example of how people use the mangrove forests of the Indus Delta.

....
(1 mark)

(ii) What impact might this human activity have on the environment in the Indus Delta?

....
(1 mark)

(c) Give two conservation strategies described in **Figure 1**. Explain their benefits.

Strategy 1 ....

The question asks you to explain so don't forget to say why the strategies help.

....

Strategy 2 ....

....
(4 marks)

(d) Describe the environmental characteristics and the wildlife of a coastal habitat you have studied.
(6 marks)

(e) For a coastal habitat you have studied, describe the strategies that have been used to ensure human activity is sustainable.
(6 marks)

Man-grow forest

Unit 2A — Population Change

Population Growth

1 Study **Figure 1**, which shows world population for the years 1500-2000.

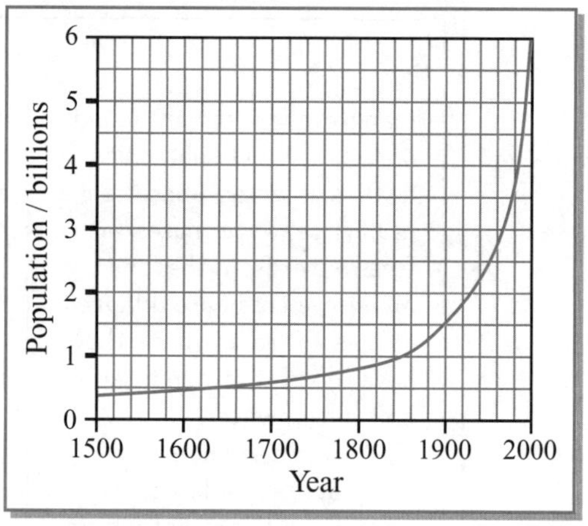

(a) (i) What was the world population in 1900?

....
(1 mark)

(ii) How many years did it take for the world population to double from 1 billion to 2 billion people?

....
(1 mark)

Figure 1

(b) Birth rate affects the population size of the world. Define the term 'birth rate'.

....
(1 mark)

2 Study **Figure 2**, which shows the Demographic Transition Model (DTM).

Figure 2

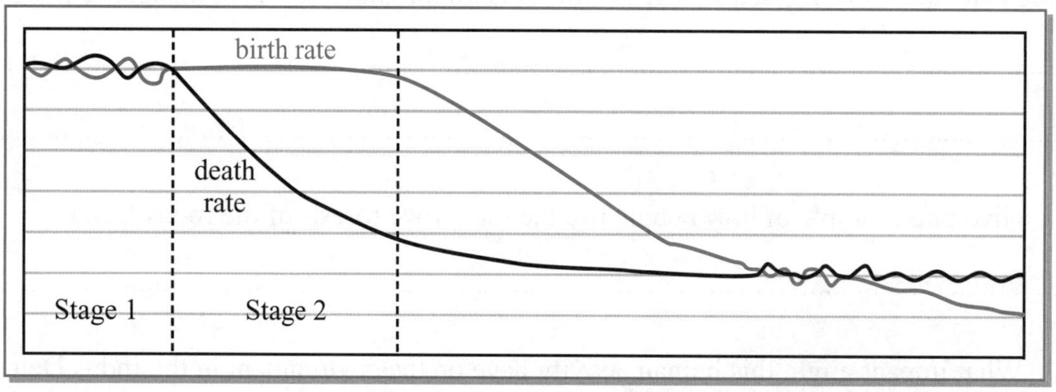

(a) Add dotted lines and labels to **Figure 2** to show when Stages 3, 4 and 5 occur.
(1 mark)

(b) (i) Using **Figure 2**, compare the death rate of a country in Stage 1 with a country in Stage 2.

Use a pencil to draw lines so you can change them if you need to.

....

....
(2 marks)

(ii) How does the size of the population change between Stages 1 and 2?

....
(1 mark)

(c) Yemen is a country in south west Asia that is poorer and less developed than the UK. Is Yemen likely to be in an earlier or a later stage of the DTM than the UK?

....
(1 mark)

Population Growth and Structure

1   Study **Figures 1a**, **1b** and **1c**, which show population pyramids for countries A, B and C.

Figure 1a — Country A   **Figure 1b — Country B** 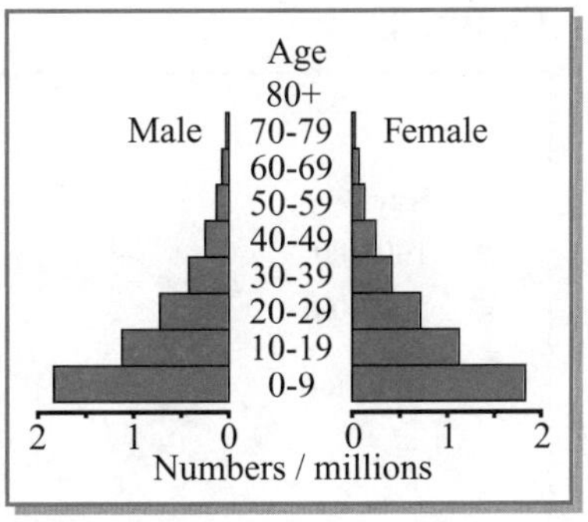   **Figure 1c — Country C**

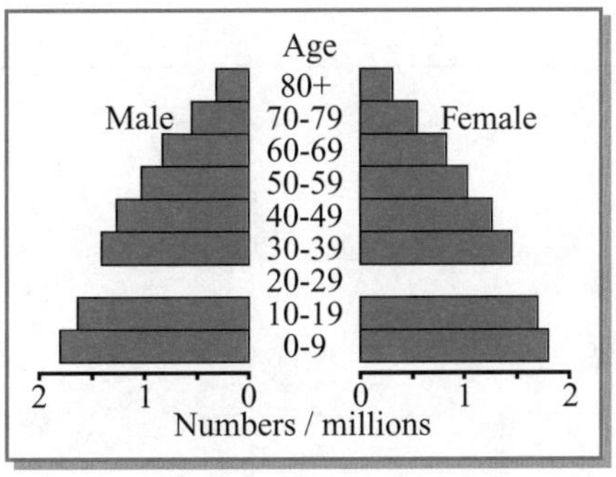

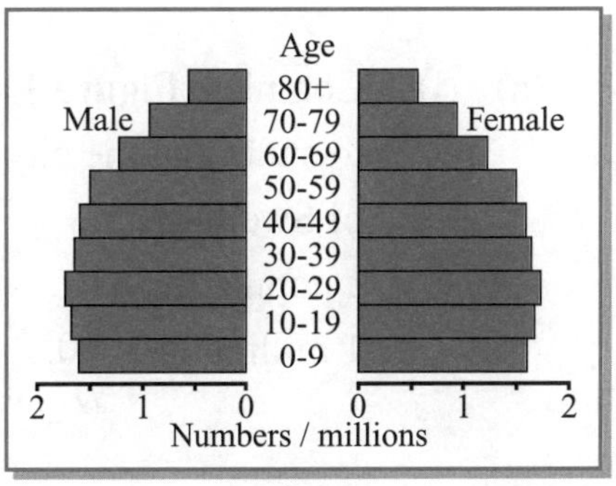

(a) Population pyramids show how many people there are
of each age group in a country. What else do they show?

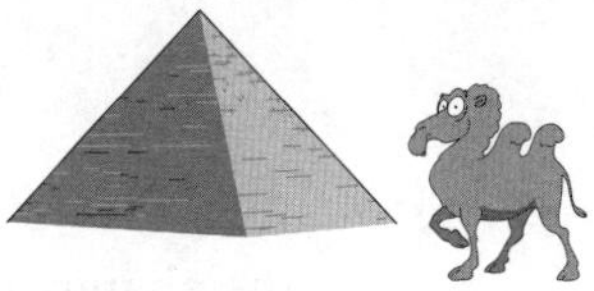

....

(1 mark)

(b) Complete **Figure 1a** to show that the population of Country A
includes 1.6 million women aged 20-29, and 1.5 million men aged 20-29.

(1 mark)

(c) Tick the correct box to show whether each of the following statements
about the population pyramids in **Figure 1** is **True** or **False**.

	True	False
The average age is higher in Country A than in Country B.	☐	☐
Country A has more people aged 0-9 than Country C.	☐	☐
Nobody in Country B lives over the age of 79.	☐	☐
There are lots more females than males in Country C.	☐	☐

(4 marks)

(d) (i)   Suggest which stage of the Demographic Transition Model (DTM) Country C is in.

....

(1 mark)

(ii)   Give two reasons for your answer to (i).

1 ....

2 ....

(2 marks)

(e) Birth rate rapidly falls in Stage 3 of the DTM. Suggest two reasons why this happens.

1 ....

2 ....

(2 marks)

Managing Rapid Population Growth

1 Study **Figure 1**, which shows how the population changed
in the region of Thirton between 1960 and 2000.

Figure 1

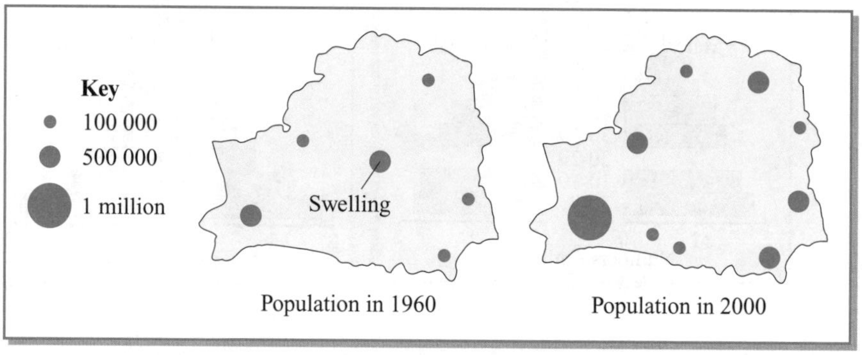

(a) (i) Complete **Figure 1**
to show that the city
of Swelling had
a population of
1 million in 2000.
(1 mark)

Key
• 100 000
● 500 000
● 1 million

Swelling

Population in 1960   Population in 2000

(ii) Tick the correct box to show whether each of the following statements about
the change in the population of Thirton shown in **Figure 1** is **True** or **False**.

	True	False
The number of people increased from 1.4 million people to 4.4 million people.	☐	☐
In 1960, there were three cities with at least 500 000 people.	☐	☐
Four settlements grew from populations of 100 000 in 1960 to 500 000 in 2000.	☐	☐

(3 marks)

(b) Rapid population growth has many impacts on a country. Describe
two social and two economic impacts of rapid population growth.

The question asks for social and economic impacts so don't put in any political impacts.

Social ....

....

Economic ....

....

(4 marks)

(c) (i) Describe a population policy that could help to address rapid population growth.

....

....

(2 marks)

(ii) Explain whether the policy described in (i) helps to achieve sustainable development.

....

....

(2 marks)

2 For a country you have studied, describe a policy used to control
rapid population growth. Explain how effective this policy has been.

(6 marks)

Managing Ageing Populations

1   Study **Figure 1**, which shows the population pyramid of a country.

(a) (i)   Tick the correct box to show whether each of
the following statements about the country
shown in **Figure 1** is **True** or **False**.

Figure 1

	True	False
The country has an ageing population.	☐	☐
There are more people over the age of 80 than under the age of 9.	☐	☐
There are more people over the age of 60 than under the age of 20.	☐	☐

(3 marks)

(ii) Which age range contains the largest number of men?

....
(1 mark)

(b) (i)   Suggest which stage of the Demographic Transition Model a country
with a population structure like that shown in **Figure 1** would be in.

....
(1 mark)

(ii) Name a country with a population structure similar to that shown in **Figure 1**.

....
(1 mark)

(c) Explain what the birth rate would be like in a country with an ageing population.

....

....
(2 marks)

(d) Ageing populations have lots of impacts which can affect the development of a country.
Describe two social and two economic impacts of an ageing population.

Social ....

....

....

Economic ....

....

....
(4 marks)

Old
people rule

Managing Ageing Populations

2 Study **Figure 2**, which shows how the population of Country A
(a nation with an ageing population) has changed between 1960 and 2008.

(a) (i) Draw a line to link each of the statements
below to complete the sentences about the
change in the population of Country A.

| From 1960 to 1980 the population | | decreased. |

| From 1980 to 2000 the population | | increased rapidly. |

| From 2000 to 2008 the population | | increased slowly. |

(2 marks)

Figure 2

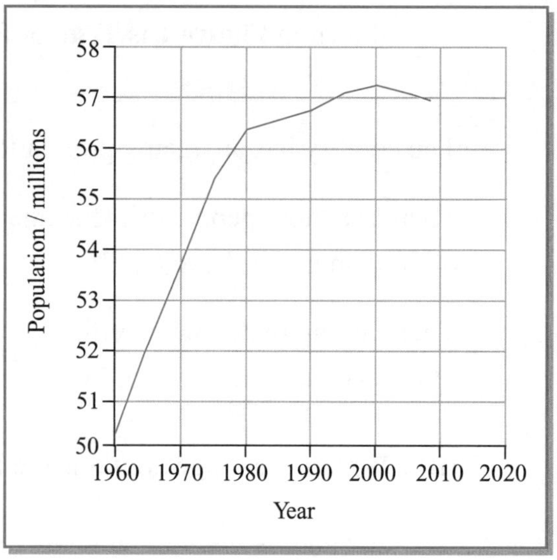

(ii) Complete **Figure 2** to show that Country A
is predicted to have a population of
57.8 million in the year 2015.

(1 mark)

(b) (i) Women in Country A are offered cash incentives to have more children.
Explain why this strategy may help to reduce the problems caused by an ageing population.

....

....

(2 marks)

(ii) Explain whether this strategy helps towards sustainable development.

....

....

(2 marks)

(c) (i) Suggest another strategy besides offering cash incentives that
could be used to manage the population of Country A.

....

(1 mark)

(ii) Explain whether the strategy suggested in (i) helps towards sustainable development or not.

....

....

(2 marks)

3 Choose one country in the European Union with an ageing population.

Name of Country ....

Read the question
carefully. Here you
need to write about
a country in the EU,
not any old country.

Describe the strategies that are being used to cope with the ageing population.

(6 marks)

Unit 2A — Population Change

Population Movements

1   Study **Figure 1**, which shows some of the yearly immigration to the UK,
    averaged over the period 1996-2000.

Figure 1

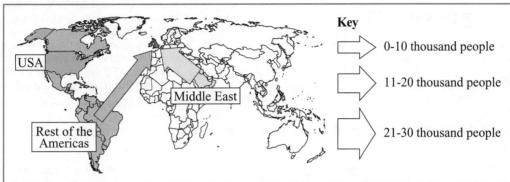

(a) (i)   What is immigration?

....
(1 mark)

(ii)   How many people migrated to the UK from the Middle East?

....
(1 mark)

(iii) Complete **Figure 1** by adding an arrow to show that
       immigration to the UK from the USA was 29 600 people.

> Use a ruler to get
> the width of the
> arrow exactly right.

(1 mark)

(b) Suggest two impacts that migration to the UK might have on the UK.

1 ....

2 ....
(2 marks)

(c) Describe two negative impacts that migration can have on a source country.

1 ....

....

2 ....

....
(2 marks)

(d) Push factors are things about a person's place of origin that makes
     them decide to move. What are pull factors? Give an example.

> It's always a good
> idea to give examples
> in your answer even
> if the question doesn't
> ask for them.

....

....

....
(2 marks)

Unit 2A — Population Change

Migration Within and To the EU

1   Study **Figure 1**, an extract from a report into migration from Poland to the UK.

(a) (i)   Using **Figure 1**, suggest two push factors that might have caused Polish people to migrate to the UK.

Figure 1

> Between 2004 and 2007 it's estimated that more than half a million Poles migrated to the UK. The reasons for migration vary from person to person, but most Polish immigrants are thought to be economic migrants who wanted to work to support their family in Poland. Unlike most EU countries, the UK doesn't have a limit to the number of immigrants it will accept from Poland.

1 ....

2 ....

(2 marks)

(ii)   Suggest one other push factor that might cause people to migrate.

....

(1 mark)

(b)   Using **Figure 1**, suggest two pull factors that caused Polish people to migrate to the UK.

1 ....

2 ....

(2 marks)

2   Study **Figure 2**, which shows the number of refugees in France and the Netherlands from 2001 to 2006.

Figure 2

Year	France	Netherlands
2001	131 601	151 928
2002	132 182	148 362
2003	130 838	140 886
2004	139 852	126 805
2005	137 316	118 189
2006	145 996	100 574

(a) (i)   What are refugees?

....

(1 mark)

(ii)   Between which years did refugee numbers in the Netherlands fall the most?

....

(1 mark)

(iii)   Complete the paragraph below to describe how the refugee population of France changed between 2001 and 2006. Choose the correct date from this list.

2001   2002   2003   2004   2005   2006

Between 2001 and .... the population stayed steady at just over 130 000. It increased to

139 852 in .... , fell to 137 316 the year after, then increased to 145 996 in ....

(3 marks)

(b)   Give two reasons why the refugees might have left their country of origin.

1 ....

2 ....

(2 marks)

(c)   For a refugee migration to the EU you have studied, describe the impacts on the receiving countries.

(6 marks)

Urbanisation

1   Study **Figure 1**, which shows the population growth of Pieville, a city in a rich country.

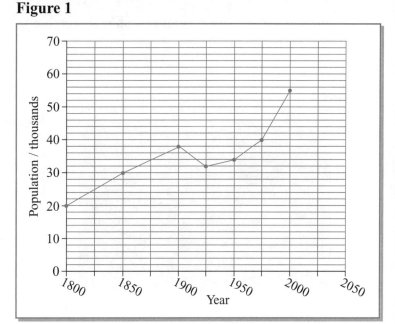

Figure 1

(a)   (i)   The population of Pieville is predicted to reach 65 000 in 2025. Complete the graph by plotting this figure.

(1 mark)

When you're completing a graph, keep it neat and readable — use a ruler, mark points with a sharp pencil, join the dots and then check it's right.

(ii)   Tick the correct box to show whether each of the following statements is **True** or **False**.

	True	False
The population increased between 1800 and 2000.	☐	☐
The population increased more rapidly from 1800 to 1900 than at any other time.	☐	☐
The population increased steadily between 1900 and 1950.	☐	☐

(3 marks)

(b)   Population change in Pieville was affected by rural-urban migration between 1800 and 1900.

(i)   What is meant by the term 'rural-urban migration'?

....
(1 mark)

(ii)   Suggest why there was an increase in rural-urban migration in richer countries between 1800 and 1900.

....

....
(2 marks)

(iii)   Suggest one reason for rural-urban migration in poorer countries.

....

....
(1 mark)

(iv)   Other than rural-urban migration, give one further cause of urbanisation.

....

....
(1 mark)

Parts of a City

1   Study **Figures 1** and **2**. **Figure 1** shows two photographs from different parts of a city. **Figure 2** is a model of a typical city viewed from above, which shows roughly where the four different parts of a city are located.

Figure 1

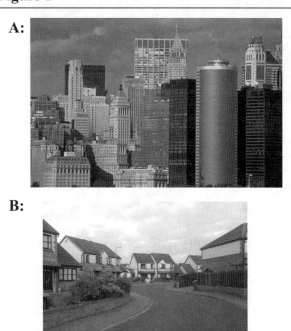

A:

B:

Figure 2

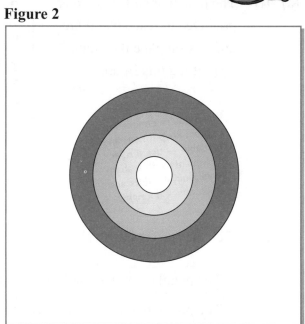

(a)   (i)   Name the parts of the city shown in the photos in **Figure 1**.

Photo A: ....   Photo B: ....
(2 marks)

(ii)   Label **Figure 2** to show where you would expect each of these parts to be found.
(2 marks)

(b)   For a city in a richer country, describe the typical land use of:

the inner city ....

....

the rural-urban fringe ....

....
(4 marks)

(c)   Suggest two ways in which the land use in a city could vary over time.

1 ....

....

2 ....

....
(2 marks)

Urban Issues

1   Study **Figure 1**, which shows state-provided housing statistics for Looptown, a city in a rich country.

Figure 1

Year	Population	State housing available	No. of people on housing list
1980	26 000	10 000	2000
1990	37 000	9000	12 000
2000	49 000	7500	23 000

(a) (i)   How many more people were on the housing list in 2000 than in 1990?

....

(1 mark)

(ii)   Describe two ways that housing shortages in rich countries can be tackled.

1 ....

....

2 ....

....

(4 marks)

(b) Study **Figure 2**, which shows the city centre of Looptown before and after redevelopment.

Figure 2

(i)   Why do some CBDs in rich countries suffer from decline?

....

....

....

The question asks why, so your answer needs to be an explanation.

....

....

(2 marks)

(ii)   Use evidence from **Figure 2** to describe two ways that the city centre has been redeveloped.

1 ....

Look for any obvious differences between the two pictures.

....

2 ....

....

(4 marks)

(c) Suggest one effect that government investment might have on a run-down city centre.

....

(1 mark)

Unit 2A — Changing Urban Environments

Urban Issues

2 Study **Figure 2**, which shows some transport statistics for an urban area.

(a) (i) How many serious traffic accidents were there in 1990?

....
(1 mark)

(ii) Describe the correlation between car ownership and serious traffic accidents.

Correlation means the relationship between two or more things.

....

....
(1 mark)

(iii) Explain the correlation identified in (i).

....

....
(1 mark)

Figure 2

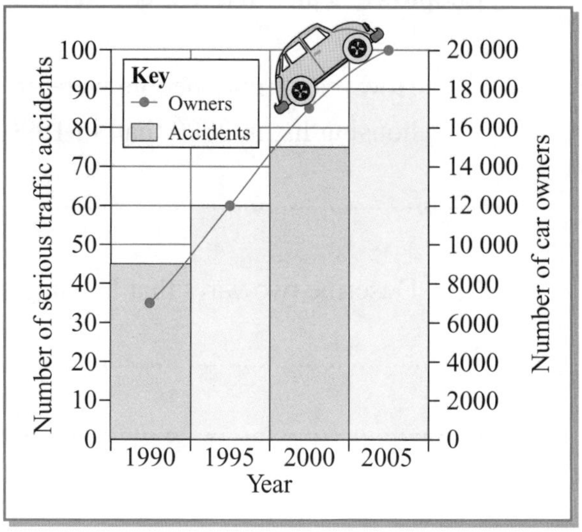

(b) Describe a strategy that could help reduce car use in urban areas.

....

....
(2 marks)

3 Study **Figure 3**, which shows the percentage of people speaking different first languages in areas of Dumblewood.

Figure 3

	First language			
Area	**English**	**Welsh**	**Hindi**	**Polish**
Trumpetville	70	12	8	10
Watertown	36	18	24	22
Sproutington	54	16	7	23

(a) Use evidence from **Figure 3** to show that there is ethnic segregation in Dumblewood.

....

Look at the percentage of people speaking each language in each area.

....

....
(2 marks)

(b) Give one cause of ethnic segregation within urban areas.

....
(1 mark)

(c) Describe two ways Dumblewood Council could support the multicultural nature of the city.

1 ....

2 ....
(2 marks)

Unit 2A — Changing Urban Environments

Squatter Settlements

1   Study **Figure 1**, a photo of a squatter settlement, and **Figure 2**, an article about the settlement.

Figure 1

©iStockphoto.com/Marcus Lindström

Figure 2

Zorbi squatter settlement has increased in size in the last 10 years. The few services that exist aren't enough for the population, and there is currently no healthcare or policing within the settlement. Some work is available but it is low paid and the hours are long. However, the government is developing Site and Service schemes to help residents and improve community spirit.

(a) (i)   What is meant by the term 'squatter settlement'?

    ....
                                                                                                              (1 mark)

    (ii)   Use **Figure 1** to describe three characteristics of a squatter settlement.

    1 ....

    2 ....

    3 ....
                                                                                                              (3 marks)

    (iii) Use **Figure 2** to describe four features of what life is like in a squatter settlement.

    1 ....

    2 ....

    3 ....

    4 ....
                                                                                                              (4 marks)

(b) Explain why squatter settlements develop in some cities in poorer countries.

    ....

    ....

    ....
                                                                                                              (2 marks)

(c) Describe how Site and Service schemes work.

    ....

    ....
                                                                                                              (2 marks)

Squatter Settlements

2 Study **Figure 3**, which is an extract from a website promoting the Can-Can Squatter Settlement Redevelopment Project.

Figure 3

The Can-Can Squatter Settlement Redevelopment Project started in 1991 to help improve life for Zorbi residents. The project involves self-help and local authority schemes including the installation of a sewage disposal system. The project also aims to improve quality of life by improving healthcare and education.

Year	Literacy rate	% people in work	% people with access to clean water	No. of people per doctor	Average life expectancy
1980	3%	27	33	2000	49
1990	3%	26	36	2000	49
2000	37%	69	73	500	57

(a) (i) Use evidence from Figure 3 to describe the effect of the Can-Can project on healthcare.

....

....

....

(3 marks)

(ii) Suggest one reason why the percentage of people with access to clean water increased between 1990 and 2000.

....

(1 mark)

(b) Describe how a self-help scheme can improve life in squatter settlements.

....

....

....

(2 marks)

(c) What are local authority schemes?

....

....

(1 mark)

3 Describe a redevelopment project in a squatter settlement you have studied. How successful has the project been?

(6 marks)

Urbanisation — Environmental Issues

1   Study **Figure 1**, which shows some statistics for a city in a poor country.

(a) (i)   The population rose to 1.9 million people in the year 2000. Complete the graph to show this.

(1 mark)

Figure 1

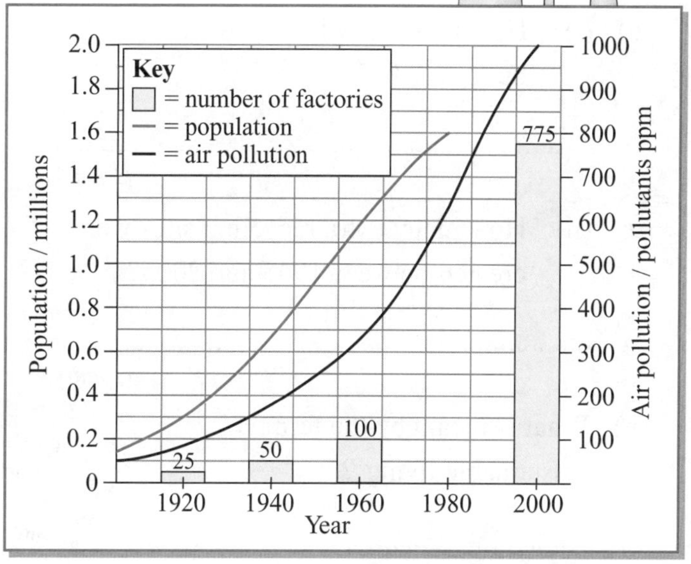

(ii) The number of factories quadrupled from 1960 to 1980. Complete the graph to show this.

(1 mark)

(b) (i)   Is the correlation between urbanisation and air pollution positive or negative?

....

(1 mark)

(ii) Explain the correlation described in part (b) (i).

....

....

....

(2 marks)

Use evidence from the Figure and what you've learnt in class to answer questions like this.

(iii) Explain how industrialisation affects air pollution.

....

....

(2 marks)

(c) (i)   Describe two environmental effects of air pollution.

1 ....

2 ....

(2 marks)

(ii) Suggest two ways that air pollution can be managed.

1 ....

2 ....

(2 marks)

(d) One of the main effects of urbanisation is the generation of large amounts of waste. Give one reason why dealing with the disposal of waste is harder for poorer countries.

....

....

(1 mark)

Unit 2A — Changing Urban Environments

Sustainable Cities

1 In 2000, Doolally City introduced a policy to encourage sustainable living.
Study **Figure 1**, which shows some Doolally statistics before and after introducing the policy.

(a) (i) How many new houses were built in 2005?

....
(1 mark)

(ii) How many extra recycling sites were created between 1995 and 2005?

....
(1 mark)

(b) What is meant by the term 'sustainable living'?

....

....

....

....
(1 mark)

Figure 1

There's a lot of information in Figure 1 so read it carefully before starting your answer.

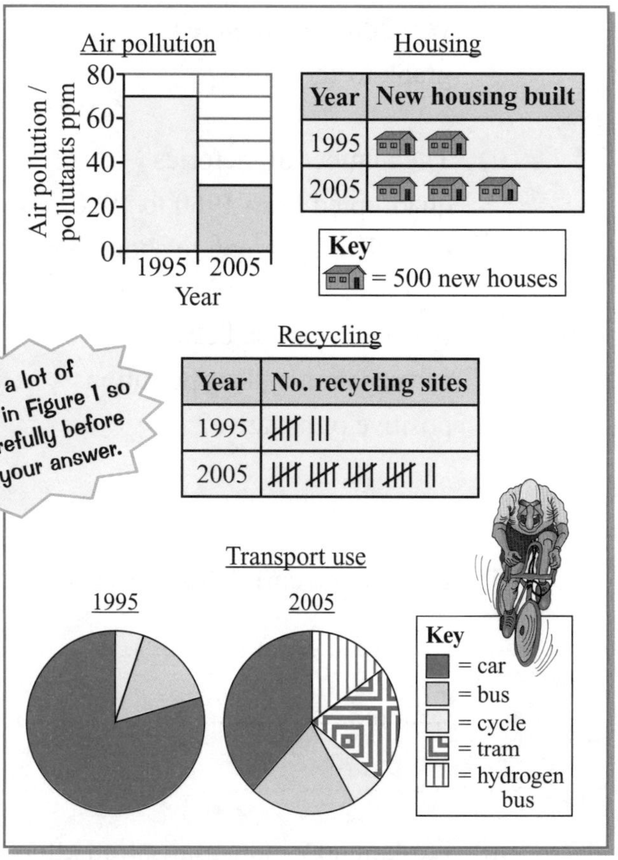

(c) (i) Complete the paragraph below to describe how changes to transport use mean that Doolally is becoming a more sustainable city. Choose the correct words from this list.

pollution   community   environment   cycle lane   public transport   acid rain

More people are using .... systems, which means there are fewer cars on

the roads. People are using methods of transport that give out less ....,

e.g. hydrogen buses. This helps make Doolally more sustainable because less damage is

done to the .... and fewer resources are used up.

(3 marks)

(ii) Use **Figure 1** to explain one other way in which Doolally is trying to be more sustainable.

....

....
(2 marks)

(d) Describe one way that new housing can be built in a sustainable way.

....
(1 mark)

2 Using a named example, describe an attempt at sustainable urban living.

(6 marks)

Change in the Rural-Urban Fringe

1 Study **Figure 1**, which shows an area of Byrnshire in 1950 and 2009.

Figure 1

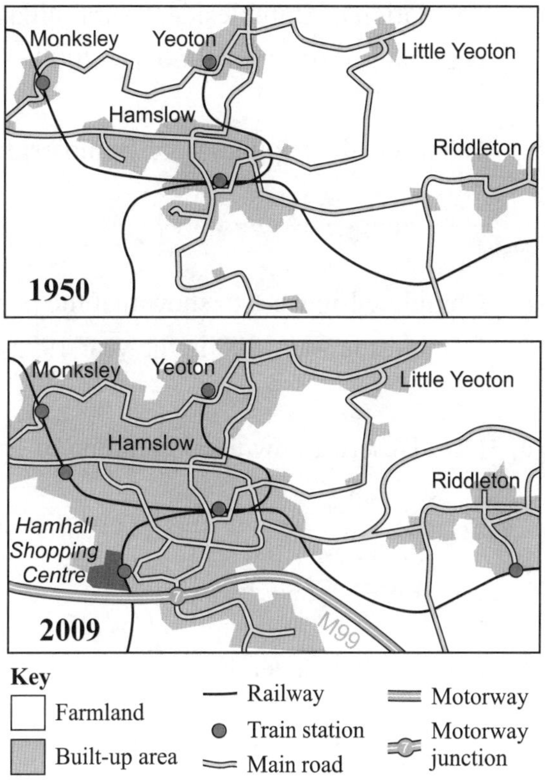

(a) (i) Tick the correct box to show whether each of the following statements about how the rural-urban fringe around Hamslow changed between 1950 and 2009 is **True** or **False**.

	True	**False**
The area of farmland increased.	☐	☐
The area that is built-up increased.	☐	☐
More main roads were built.	☐	☐
Four new train stations were built.	☐	☐

(4 marks)

(ii) Describe two impacts these changes may have had on the rural-urban fringe.

....

....

....

(2 marks)

(b) Riddleton is a commuter village on the outskirts of Hamslow.

(i) What is a commuter village?

....

....

(1 mark)

(ii) Give one way in which transport links to Riddleton improved between 1950 and 2009.

....

(1 mark)

(iii) Explain why improved transport links to Riddleton caused the village to increase in size.

....

(1 mark)

(iv) Give two common characteristics of growing villages.

1 ....

2 ....

(2 marks)

Change in Rural Areas

1 Study **Figure 1**, which shows how the population of Bumbleside, a rural village, has changed between 1950 and 2000.

Figure 1

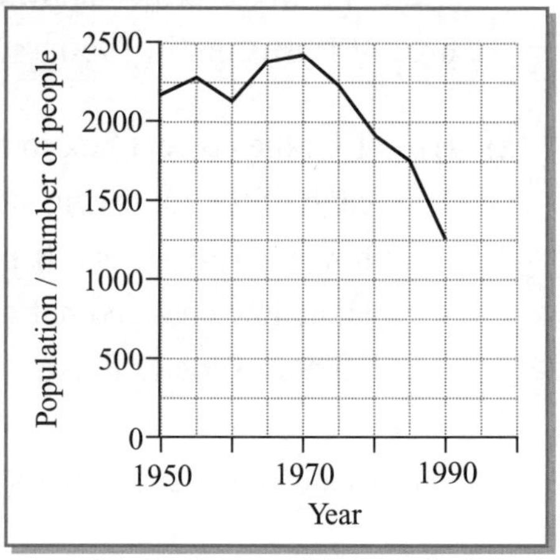

(a) What was the population of Bumbleside in 1985?

....
(1 mark)

(b) Complete **Figure 1** to show that the population of Bumbleside was 1000 in the year 1995 and 500 in 2000.
(2 marks)

(c) (i) Describe how the population of Bumbleside changed between 1970 and 2000.

Read off numbers from the graph to use in your answer.

....

....
(1 mark)

(ii) In 1970, a nearby mine closed. Explain how this may have caused the population change.

....

....
(1 mark)

2 Study **Figure 2**, an advert for a house for sale in a rural village.

(a) Loreton is a declining village. Using the information in **Figure 2** and your own knowledge, describe two characteristics of declining villages.

1 ....

2 ....
(2 marks)

Figure 2

Sunnyside cottage

A charming converted barn located in Loreton, a small peaceful village popular with second home owners.
Set in stunning countryside, shops and other amenities are just a 30 minute drive away. Note: Public transport is limited in this area — own car recommended.

(b) A high percentage of the houses in Loreton are second homes. Complete the paragraph below to explain why this might have led to no shops in the village. Choose the correct words from the following list.

larger   higher   smaller   decreased   increased   lower

The popularity of second homes may have .... houses prices in the

area, forcing young local people to move away as they couldn't afford to live

there. The permanent population would be .... so the demand for

services like shops would be ...., and they'd eventually close.
(3 marks)

3 Describe the causes and impacts of depopulation of a named rural area in the UK.
(6 marks)

Change in UK Commercial Farming

1 Study **Figure 1**, showing the use of an area of agricultural land in 1950 and in 2000.

Figure 1

Key

Farm ■

Farm boundary

Fields:
- Wheat
- Barley
- Potatoes

(a) Complete **Figure 1** to show that field A was used for growing wheat in 1950.

(1 mark)

(b) (i) How has farming in the area changed between 1950 and 2000? Circle the correct word in each sentence.

Farms have **increased** / **decreased** in size.

Each farm is growing **more** / **fewer** types of crop.

Fields have become **larger** / **smaller**.

(3 marks)

(ii) Explain two ways in which these changes could have a negative impact on the environment.

1 ....

....

2 ....

....

(2 marks)

(iii) Describe one other way modern farming practices negatively affect the environment.

....

(1 mark)

2 Study **Figure 2**, an extract from an article about a farm.

Figure 2

(a) What is the name of the type of farming carried out on Hilltop Farm?

....

(1 mark)

(b) Using information from **Figure 2** and your own knowledge, give two reasons why demand for produce from this type of farm is increasing.

....

....

....

(2 marks)

> No artificial pesticides or fertilisers are used on Hilltop Farm, and despite producing lower yields than its neighbours, Hilltop continues to make a good profit. This is partly due to increased demand for its produce, and partly thanks to government policies that encourage environmentally-friendly farming.

(c) Describe a government policy that aims to reduce the environmental impact of farming.

....

....

(2 marks)

Change in UK Commercial Farming

3 Study **Figure 3**, which shows how the quantity and source of food consumed in Byrnshire has changed between 1960 and 2000.

Figure 3

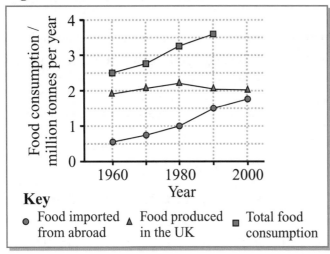

Key
- Food imported from abroad
- ▲ Food produced in the UK
- ■ Total food consumption

(a) Complete **Figure 3** to show that 3.75 million tonnes of food was consumed in Byrnshire in 2000.
(1 mark)

(b) Calculate the percentage of the total food consumed in Byrnshire in 2000 that was produced in the UK.

....

....
(1 mark)

(c) Tick the correct box to show whether each of the following statements about how the nature of food consumption in Byrnshire has changed is **True** or **False**.

	True	False
Total food consumption increased from 1960 to 2000.	☐	☐
The amount of food produced in the UK decreased from 1960 to 1980.	☐	☐
The amount of food imported from abroad increased from 1980 to 2000.	☐	☐

(3 marks)

(d) Suggest how the changes shown by **Figure 3** have benefited consumers in Byrnshire.

....
(1 mark)

(e) Imported food is often cheaper than food produced in the UK. Explain how this might affect UK farmers.

....

....
(2 marks)

(f) 69% of all food in Byrnshire is purchased from supermarkets. Explain why this forces farmers to keep their prices low.

....

....
(1 mark)

4 Describe how farming practices have changed in one commercial farming area in the UK that you have studied.

(6 marks)

Sustainable Rural Living

1 Study **Figure 1**, which is an extract from an article about Community Rail Partnerships.

(a) What does the term 'sustainable living' mean?

....

....

....

....

(2 marks)

Figure 1

Local Railway Cash Success

The Ecklethwaite - Nabstable Support Group is celebrating today after receiving a grant of £5000 from the government-run Community Rail Partnership. The money is to be spent on improved cycle storage facilities at Ecklethwaite station, and a shelter for rail and connecting bus passengers.

A spokesman said "Community Rail Partnerships aim to increase local train use by improving bus links, cycle routes and station buildings, to promote more sustainable living in rural areas".

(b) Community Rail Partnerships aim to increase the use of trains. This will reduce the number of people travelling by car. Explain two ways in which fewer people travelling by car may help towards more sustainable living in rural areas.

....

....

....

(2 marks)

(c) Describe one other government initiative that protects the rural economy and environment.

....

....

....

Don't waste time describing more than one initiative.

....

(4 marks)

2 Study **Figure 2**, which shows potato yields for fields with different amounts of irrigation.

Figure 2

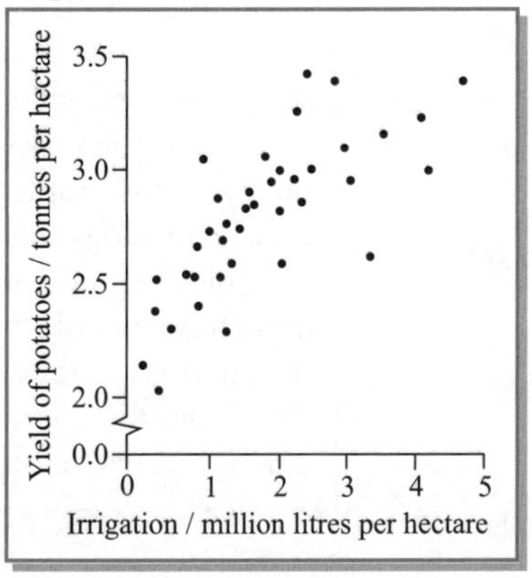

(a) Does **Figure 2** show a positive or a negative correlation?

....

(1 mark)

(b) Suggest why irrigation is sometimes unsustainable.

....

(1 mark)

(c) Suggest two ways, other than by reducing irrigation, that farming can be done more sustainably.

....

....

(2 marks)

Unit 2A — Changing Rural Environments

Changes to Farming in Tropical Areas

1   Study **Figure 1** which shows the changing nature of farming in Lartua between 1960 and 2000. Lartua is a poor rural area in the tropics.

Figure 1

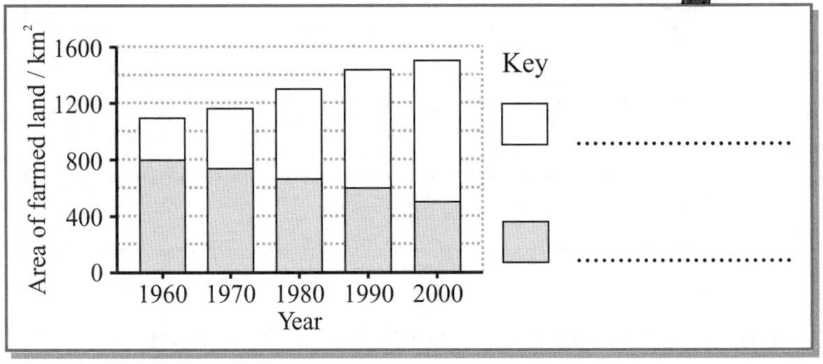

(a) (i)   Complete the key for **Figure 1** by adding 'subsistence farming' and 'commercial farming' in the correct places.

(1 mark)

(ii)   What is commercial farming?

....

(1 mark)

(iii)   How much land was used for commercial farming in Lartua in 2000?....................................

(1 mark)

(b) (i)   Tick the correct box to show whether each of the following statements about how the nature of farming in Lartua has changed is **True** or **False**.

	True	False
The total area of land farmed decreased from 1960 to 2000.	☐	☐
The area of land used for subsistence farming increased from 1960 to 2000.	☐	☐
The area of land used for commercial farming increased from 1960 to 2000.	☐	☐

(3 marks)

(ii)   Suggest one impact of the change to commercial farming in the area.

....

....

(1 mark)

2   Study **Figure 2**, which gives information about an appropriate technology used in Lesotho, a small country in southern Africa.

Figure 2

Farmers in Lesotho have benefited from drip irrigation, which uses a network of pipes to slowly supply water from a tank directly to the roots of plants. This simple, low cost technology means much less water is wasted, and allows people to grow fruit and vegetables for their household even during the dry season.

(a)   Explain why the technique outlined in **Figure 2** can be described as an appropriate technology.

....

(1 mark)

(b)   Describe another example of an appropriate technology that has been used to increase food production.

....

....

(3 marks)

Unit 2A — Changing Rural Environments

Changes to Farming in Tropical Areas

3   Study **Figure 3**, which shows how irrigation levels have changed
     in Bangolo, a rural region located in a tropical climate.

Figure 3

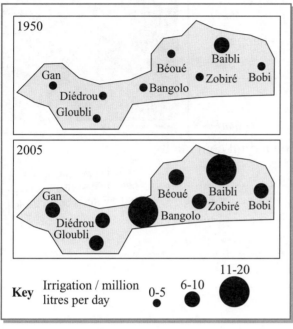

Key Irrigation / million litres per day   0-5   6-10   11-20

(a) (i) How much water was used for
          irrigation in Gan in 2005?

     ....
     (1 mark)

     (ii) Irrigation increased in all areas between
           1950 and 2005. Give a reason, other
           than a decrease in rainfall, that could
           have caused this trend.

     ....

     ....

     ....
     (1 mark)

(b) (i) Describe one positive impact that irrigation can have on the environment.

     ....

     ....
     (1 mark)

     (ii) Describe two negative impacts that irrigation can have on the environment.

     1 ....

     2 ....
     (2 marks)

(c) Give two ways in which irrigation might have improved people's lives in Bangolo.

     1 ....

     2 ....
     (2 marks)

(d) Increased irrigation can increase the percentage of people
     infected with malaria, due to mosquitoes breeding in
     irrigation ditches. Study **Figure 4**, which shows the
     percentage of people in Bangolo that were infected in
     1950 and in 2005. What was the percentage difference
     between those infected in 1950 and 2005?

Figure 4

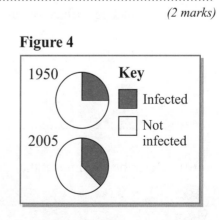

1950   **Key**
        ■ Infected
        □ Not
          infected
2005

     ....
     (1 mark)

Unit 2A — Changing Rural Environments

Factors Affecting Farming in Tropical Areas

1   Study **Figure 1**, which shows an area of agricultural land in a tropical region.

(a) (i)   Name the process that is occurring in **Figure 1**.

....

(1 mark)

(ii) How can overgrazing cause this process to happen?

....

....

(1 mark)

Figure 1

©iStockphoto.com/ Sandra Dunlap

(b) Explain two impacts this process could have on a rural community.

1 ....

....

2 ....

....

(2 marks)

> To answer this question you need to describe the impacts and say how the process leads to them.

2   Study **Figure 2**, which shows land use and migration of people in the tropical Kolurna region.

(a) Name the type of migration shown in **Figure 2**.

....

(1 mark)

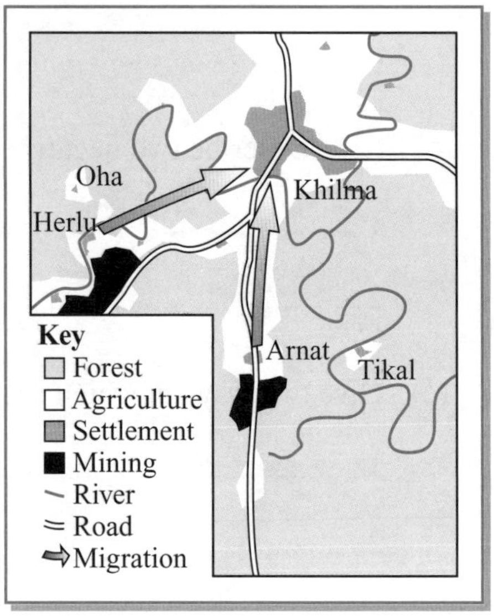

(b) (i)   Many people are migrating from Herlu due to the impact of nearby mining. Describe one way mining can affect subsistence farming.

....

....

....

(1 mark)

Figure 2

Key
☐ Forest
☐ Agriculture
▨ Settlement
■ Mining
~ River
= Road
⇨ Migration

(ii) Name another human activity that can affect farming.   ....

(1 mark)

(iii) Explain one way the activity you named in part (b) (ii) can affect subsistence farming.

....

....

(2 marks)

(c) Describe one impact that the migration shown in **Figure 1** might have on the city of Khilma.

....

(1 mark)

Measuring Development

1 Study **Figure 1**, which shows measures of development for Canada, Taiwan and Angola.

Figure 1

	Canada	Taiwan	Angola
GNI per capita✱	$32 220	$22 900	$2210
Birth rate	10.3	9.0	43.7
Death rate	7.7	6.8	24.1
Infant mortality rate	5.0	5.4	180.2
Life expectancy	81.2	78.0	38.2
Literacy rate	99.0%	96.1%	67.4%

✱ GNI per capita information from Hutchinson Country Facts. © RM, 2009.
All rights reserved. Helicon Publishing is a division of RM.

(a) What is meant by the Gross National Income (GNI) per capita of a country?

....

....

....

(2 marks)

(b) (i) Define birth rate.

....

(1 mark)

(ii) Does birth rate increase or decrease as a country becomes more developed? Circle the correct answer.

Increases   **Decreases**

(1 mark)

(c) (i) Which country shown in **Figure 1** is the most developed?

....

(1 mark)

(ii) Explain your answer to (c) (i).

'Explain' means you need to give reasons.

....

....

(2 marks)

(d) Give two limitations of using a single measure of development to judge how developed a country is.

Limitation 1 ....

....

Limitation 2 ....

....

(2 marks)

(e) Why is the HDI a useful measure of development?

....

....

(1 mark)

Global Inequalities

1 Study **Figure 1**, which shows the global distribution of MEDCs and LEDCs.

Figure 1

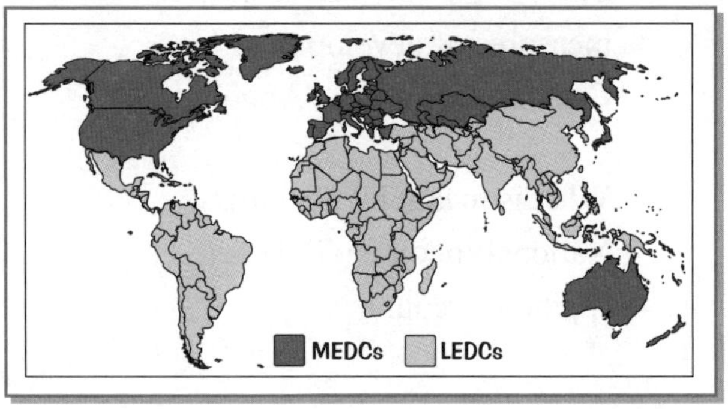

MEDCs LEDCs

(a) Complete the sentences below to describe the distribution of LEDCs and MEDCs. Choose the correct words from this list.

| middle | south | USA | north |
| equator | Australia | top | south |

MEDCs are generally found in the ...., e.g. the USA, Canada and European countries.

However, some MEDCs are found in the ...., e.g. .... and New Zealand.

LEDCs are generally found in the ...., e.g. Brazil and all the African countries.

(4 marks)

(b) Give one problem with classifying countries as MEDCs or LEDCs.

....

(1 mark)

(c) Apart from LEDCs and MEDCs, describe two other categories used to classify countries.

1 ....

Name the category, then briefly write about what it's like.

....

2 ....

....

(4 marks)

Figure 2

2 Study **Figure 2**, which shows the PQLI (Physical Quality of Life Index, an indicator of quality of life) and the number of mobile phones per 1000 people (an indicator of standard of living) in two countries.

	UK	Mozambique
PQLI	99.9	28.4
Number of mobile phones per 1000 people	1236.5	203.3

(a) Tick the correct box to show whether each of the following statements is **True** or **False**.

True **False**

Quality of life is higher in the UK than in Mozambique. ☐ ☐

Standard of living is higher in Mozambique than in the UK. ☐ ☐

(2 marks)

(b) Explain the difference between standard of living and quality of life.

....

....

(2 marks)

Causes of Global Inequalities

1 Study **Figure 1**, which shows the percentage of people with access to clean water and the HDI values of four countries in 2006-2007.

Figure 1

	% of population with access to clean water	HDI
Chad	48	0.389
Ethiopia	42	0.389
Uganda	64	0.493
Pakistan	90	0.562

(a) Compare the percentage of the population who have access to clean water in Pakistan and Ethiopia.

....

....

(1 mark)

(b) Complete the paragraph below to explain how the availability of clean water in a country affects its development. Choose the correct words from this list.

more	**HDI**	**globalisation**	**development**	**waterborne**
work	**airborne**	**less**	**quality of life**	**medical**

A country with limited access to clean water will be .... developed.

This is because if the only water people can drink is dirty they'll get ill due to

.... diseases and this will reduce their ....

Ill people can't work so they don't add money to the economy and they also cost money to treat.

This means the country will have less money to spend on ....

(4 marks)

2 **Figure 2**

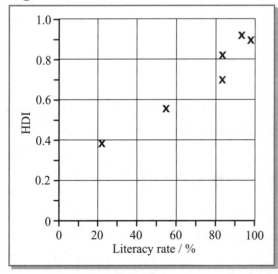

Study **Figure 2**, which is a scatter graph showing the HDI value and literacy rate for six countries in 2006.

(a) Is the correlation between literacy rate and development positive or negative?

....

(1 mark)

(b) The literacy rate in Mali in 2006 was 22.9. What was its HDI score?

....

(1 mark)

(c) A low literacy rate shows that a country's population is poorly educated. Suggest why a poorly educated population would lead to a low level of development.

....

....

(2 marks)

Unit 2B — The Development Gap

Causes of Global Inequalities

3   Tsunamis are natural hazards that can affect a country's development.
Study **Figure 3**, a photograph taken in Indonesia after a tsunami.

(a) (i)   Give one impact of the tsunami that can
be seen in **Figure 3**.

Figure 3

©iStockphoto.com/Justin Long

....
(1 mark)

(ii)   What is meant by the term 'natural hazard'?

....

....
(1 mark)

(b) For an area you have studied, explain how a natural disaster has affected its development.

(6 marks)

4   In 2007, Nicaragua had a 0.01% share of the world's total exports while the UK had
a 3.04% share. Study **Figure 4**, which shows the types of goods exported by each country.

Figure 4

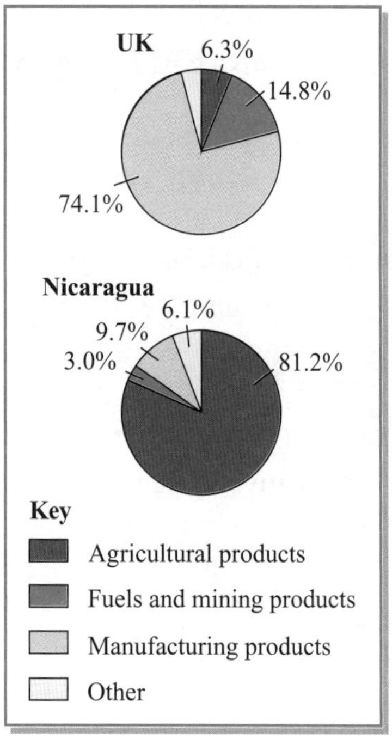

UK 6.3%
14.8%
74.1%

Nicaragua 6.1%
9.7%
3.0%   81.2%

Key
■ Agricultural products
■ Fuels and mining products
■ Manufacturing products
□ Other

(a) (i)   In 2007, Nicaragua generated US$1225 million from
exports. Using **Figure 4**, calculate how much money was
generated from the export of fuels and mining products.

....
(1 mark)

Include your working for any calculations.

(ii)   In 2007, what percentage of UK
exports was not agricultural products,
fuels or mining products?

....
(1 mark)

(iii) Tick the correct box to show whether each of following
statements applies to the UK or to Nicaragua.

	UK	Nicaragua
Exports mostly primary products.	□	□
Exports a high percentage of manufacturing products.	□	□
Has little money to spend on development.	□	□

(3 marks)

(b) Explain how poor trade links affect a country's development.

....

....
(2 marks)

Causes of Global Inequalities

5   Study **Figure 5**, which shows the change in HDI for three countries between 1990 and 2005.

Figure 5

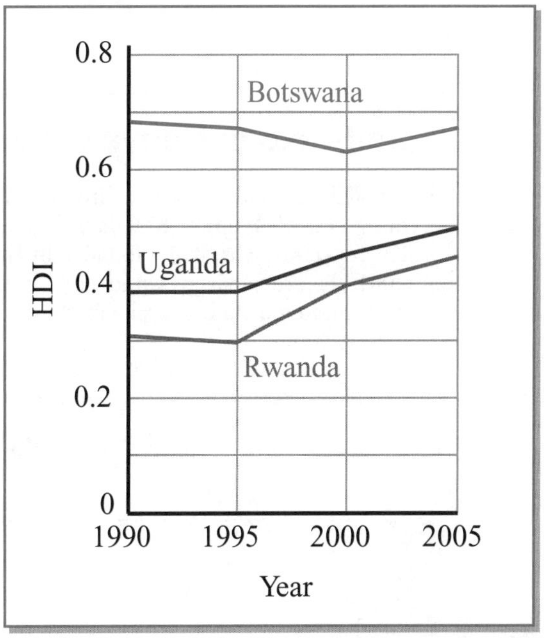

(a) (i)   What was the HDI for Rwanda in 1995?

....
(1 mark)

(ii)   Describe how the HDI for Botswana changed between 1990 and 2005.

....

Make sure you refer to the figure in your answer — mention specific HDI values for different years.

....

....

....
(2 marks)

(b) (i)   Rwanda has a history of civil war.
Is war likely to increase or decrease a country's level of development?

....
(1 mark)

(ii)   Give two reasons for your answer to (i).

Reason 1 ....

....

Reason 2 ....

....
(2 marks)

(c)   Egypt's HDI increased steadily from 0.58 to 0.70 between 1990 and 2005.

(i)   Was Egypt's HDI higher or lower than Uganda's between 1990 and 2005?

....
(1 mark)

(ii)   Egypt has very low rainfall. Draw a line to link **each** of the statements about the impacts of low rainfall to their potential effect on development.

Impact

It is hard to produce a lot of food

People have fewer crops to sell

The government gets less money from taxes

Effect on development

People have less money to spend on goods and services

The government has less money to spend on development

This can lead to malnutrition and people who are malnourished have a low quality of life

(2 marks)

Unit 2B — The Development Gap

Reducing Global Inequality

1 Study **Figure 1**, a newspaper article about a self-help scheme in Kenya.

Figure 1

Self-help in Kenya's slums

The Kibera Youth Self-Help Group (KYSG) is on a mission to clear up the Kianda village area of the Kibera slums. Originally founded by three men in 2001, the group has grown to work with around 200 children including orphans, street kids and jobless youths.

One of the first things the group did was to clear up the community dumping area. They started a solid waste collection scheme and disposed of the waste responsibly in designated areas. They've followed it up with a recycling scheme to collect and sell plastic waste. The group's offices are based on the old dumping ground, which now also boasts car washing bays and carpet cleaning facilities.

(a) Describe two ways in which KYSG's activities are improving quality of life for people in Kibera.

....

....

....

(2 marks)

(b) Suggest two other ways people in poor areas try to improve their own quality of life.

....

....

(2 marks)

2 Study **Figure 2**, which shows the annual income of a farmer in Mali between 1994 and 2002. He joined a fair trade co-operative in 1996.

Figure 2

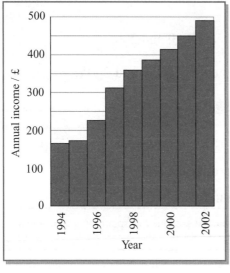

(a) (i) What was the farmer's income in 1999?

....

(1 mark)

(ii) Did joining the fair trade scheme have a positive or negative effect on the farmer's income?

....

(1 mark)

(b) Describe two ways in which fair trade schemes can benefit poorer countries.

....

....

....

....

(2 marks)

Reducing Global Inequality

3 The North American Free Trade Agreement (NAFTA) is a trading group that was set up in 1994 to eliminate trade barriers between the USA, Canada and Mexico. Study **Figure 3**, which shows the value of exports and imports between NAFTA countries in 1993 and 2008.

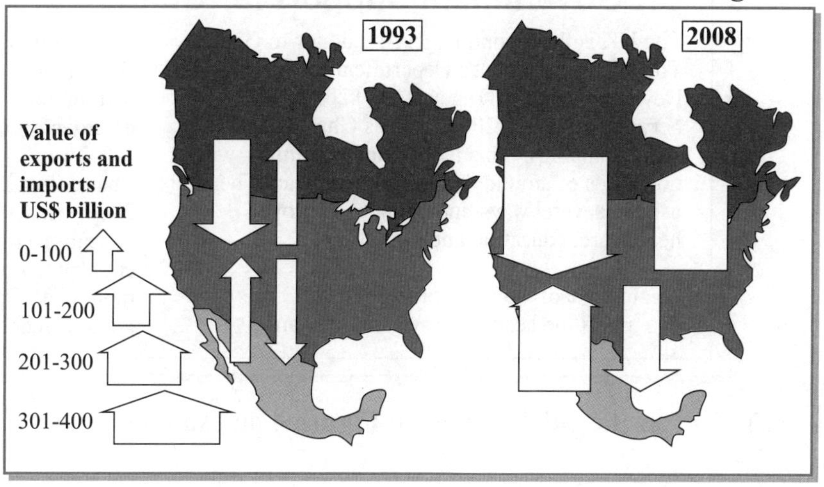

(a) (i) What was the value of USA exports to Mexico in 2008?

Figure 3

Make sure you read the key carefully and get the units right.

....

....

(1 mark)

(ii) How did the value of USA exports to Canada change between 1993 and 2008?

....

(1 mark)

(iii) Using **Figure 3**, complete the paragraph below to explain how joining NAFTA may have affected Mexico's development. Choose the correct words from this list.

development   buying   decreased   imports   trading   increased

Figure 3 shows that between 1993 and 2008 exports from Mexico to the US ....

This means that the amount of money Mexico made from .... would have

increased, so the country would have had more money to spend on ....

(3 marks)

(b) Describe how trading groups can cause problems for poorer non-member countries.

....

....

(2 marks)

4 Bolivia was one of the first countries to make a conservation swap agreement. The agreement with Conservation International in 1987 led to the cancellation of $650 000 of debt.

(a) What is a conservation swap?

....

(1 mark)

(b) Suggest how the conservation swap agreement could have affected Bolivia's development.

....

....

(2 marks)

Reducing Global Inequality

5   Study **Figure 4**, a newspaper article about an aid project in Ghana.

Figure 4

UK Government Support for Ghana

The UK is the second largest aid donor to Ghana. The UK Government's Department for International Development (DFID) gave over £205 million between 2005 and 2007 towards Ghana's poverty reduction plans. This level of aid continues, with donations of around £85 million per year. The aid is used in several ways, including to improve healthcare, education and sanitation.

About 15% of the UK's funding in 2008 was used to support the healthcare system in Ghana —

£42.5 million was pledged to support the Ghanaian Government's 2008-2012 health plan. On top of that, in 2008 the UK gave nearly £7 million to buy emergency equipment to reduce maternal deaths.

Thanks to a £105 million grant from the UK in 2006, Ghana has been able to set up a ten year education strategic plan. It was the first African country to do this. The UK pledged additional money to help 12 000 children in North Ghana to get a formal basic education.

(a) (i)   Is the aid described in **Figure 4** an example of multilateral aid or bilateral aid?

....

(1 mark)

(ii)   Suggest the potential advantages for the receiving country of long-term aid projects such as the one described in **Figure 4**.

This is a 2 mark question, so try to come up with two advantages.

....

....

(2 marks)

(iii) Give one potential disadvantage for the receiving country of long-term aid projects.

....

(1 mark)

(b) (i)   Explain what is meant by sustainable aid.

....

....

(2 marks)

(ii)   Is the aid project described in **Figure 4** sustainable?

....

(1 mark)

(c) What is meant by 'short-term aid'?

....

(1 mark)

(d) Give one disadvantage of aid projects for the donor country.

....

(1 mark)

(e) Explain how a development project you have studied is benefiting the receiving country.

(6 marks)

Inequalities in the EU

1   The European Union's Regional Development Fund (ERDF) invests money in sustainable development projects in urban areas. Study **Figure 1**, which shows the locations of URBAN Community Initiative development projects in the UK that received a contribution from the ERDF programmes of 1994-1999 and 2000-2006.

Figure 1

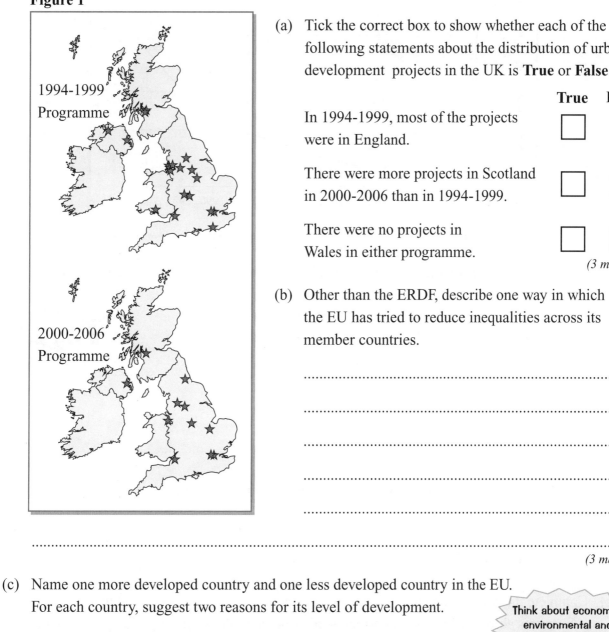

(a) Tick the correct box to show whether each of the following statements about the distribution of urban development projects in the UK is **True** or **False**.

	True	False
In 1994-1999, most of the projects were in England.	☐	☐
There were more projects in Scotland in 2000-2006 than in 1994-1999.	☐	☐
There were no projects in Wales in either programme.	☐	☐

(3 marks)

(b) Other than the ERDF, describe one way in which the EU has tried to reduce inequalities across its member countries.

....

....

....

....

....

....

(3 marks)

(c) Name one more developed country and one less developed country in the EU. For each country, suggest two reasons for its level of development.

> Think about economic, environmental and political reasons.

More developed country ....

1 ....

2 ....

Less developed country ....

1 ....

2 ....

(4 marks)

Unit 2B — The Development Gap

Globalisation Basics

1 Improvements in air transport are partly responsible for the increase in globalisation.
Study **Figure 1**, which shows the number of passengers using UK airports from 1950 to 2000.

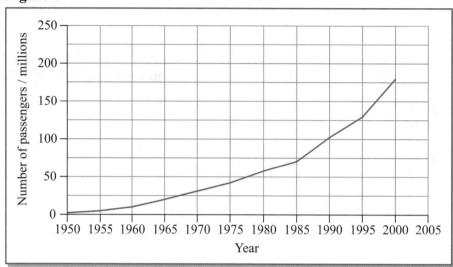

Figure 1

(a) (i) Complete **Figure 1** to show that 228 million passengers used UK airports in 2005.

(1 mark)

(ii) Using **Figure 1**, calculate the difference between the number
of passengers using UK airports in 1960 and in 2000.

....

(1 mark)

(b) (i) What is meant by the term 'globalisation'?

....

(1 mark)

(ii) Explain how improvements in air transport have increased globalisation.

....

....

(2 marks)

(c) Complete the paragraph below to explain why many companies have moved their
call centres abroad. Choose the correct words from the following list.

| reduce | ICT | increase |
| cheaper | expensive | transport |

Put a line through words that you've used so you know which ones you have left.

Improvements in .... mean it's just as easy for people to phone a faraway

country as their own. This has allowed some call centres to move abroad where labour is

..............................., helping to .... running costs.

(3 marks)

Trans-National Corporations (TNCs)

1   Study **Figure 1**, which shows the distribution of Mega Lomania (a TNC) around the world.

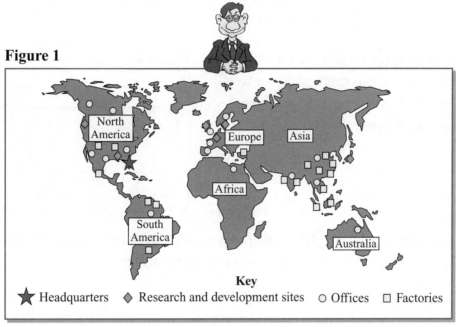

Figure 1

Key
★ Headquarters   ◆ Research and development sites   ○ Offices   □ Factories

(a)   What is meant by the term 'Trans-National Corporation' (TNC)?

....

(1 mark)

(b)   Draw a line to link each of the statements to complete the sentences
describing and explaining the distribution of Mega Lomania's sites.

Headquarters, research and development sites and most offices are located in	cheaper labour, so more profit can be made by locating there.
Most factories are located in	richer countries, e.g. in Europe.
Richer countries have	more people with administrative and research skills.
Poorer countries have	poorer countries, e.g. in Asia.

(3 marks)

(c)   Give two advantages of TNCs locating in places like south east Asia.

....

....

(2 marks)

(d)   How do TNCs like Mega Lomania increase globalisation?

....

(1 mark)

2   Describe the advantages brought to different countries by a TNC that you have studied.

(6 marks)

Change in Manufacturing Location

1 Mega Lomania has moved all of its factories from Ingerland (a rich country)
to Bonechina (a Newly Industrialising Country). Study **Figure 1**,
which compares working conditions in the two countries.

(a) (i) Using **Figure 1**, calculate the difference
between the maximum wage per week
for a factory worker in Ingerland
and Bonechina.

Figure 1

	Ingerland	Bonechina
Minimum wage / hour	£6.12	£0.63
Maximum number of working hours per week	40	80
Health and safety	Very strict	Very lax

....

....

(2 marks)

(ii) Complete the paragraph below to suggest why Mega Lomania has moved its factories
to Bonechina. Choose the correct words from this list.

triple	improving	increases	reduces
Ingerland	**worsening**	**double**	**Bonechina**

The minimum wage is much lower in Bonechina. This .... the cost of

manufacturing because factory workers are paid less. The maximum number of working

hours in Bonechina is .... the maximum in Ingerland, so more products can be

made in a day. Health and safety is very lax in .... This lowers the cost of

manufacturing goods because less money is spent on .... the safety of factories.

(4 marks)

(iii) Suggest one other reason why factories are moved to Newly Industrialising Countries.

....

(1 mark)

(b) Many other TNCs are moving their factories out of Ingerland to
countries like Bonechina. This is leading to deindustrialisation.

Make sure you know the definitions of tricky geographical words.

(i) Describe what is meant by 'deindustrialisation'.

....

(1 mark)

(ii) Describe two effects of deindustrialisation on countries like Ingerland.

....

....

(2 marks)

2 Explain the recent growth in manufacturing in China.

(6 marks)

Globalisation and Energy Demand

1   Study **Figure 1**, which shows the world's actual and predicted energy consumption.

(a)   Complete **Figure 1** to show that the world's predicted energy consumption in 2025 will be 640 quadrillion Btu.

(1 mark)

Figure 1

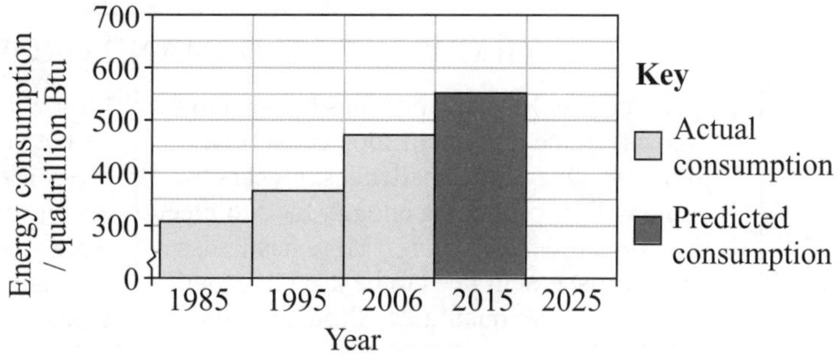

(b)   (i)   Globalisation has increased the wealth of some poorer countries. Explain how this has increased the global demand for energy.

....

(1 mark)

(ii)   Give one other reason why the global demand for energy is increasing.

....

(1 mark)

(c)   Study **Figure 2**, which shows the potential sites for new nuclear power plants in the UK.

Figure 2

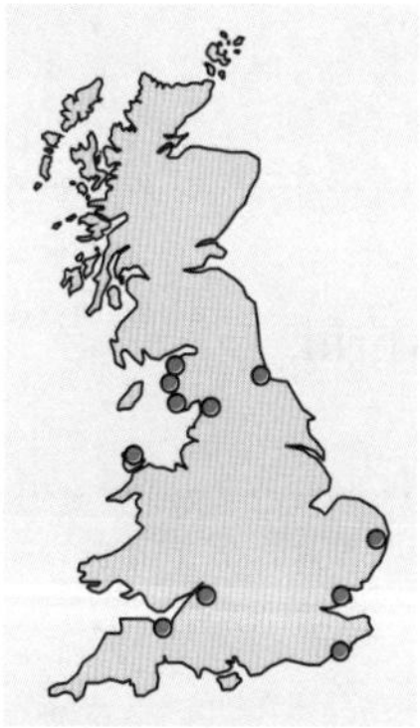

Key

• Potential nuclear power plant site

(i)   Tick the correct box next to the sentence that best describes the distribution of the sites around the UK.

Most sites are located in central England and Wales. ☐

Most sites are in eastern England. ☐

All sites are near the coast and none are in Scotland. ☐

(1 mark)

(ii)   Give two social impacts of building more nuclear power plants.

Remember, impacts don't have to be negative.

....

....

....

(2 marks)

(d)   Tick the correct box to show whether each of the following statements is **True** or **False**.

	True	False
Using more fossil fuels will increase acid rainfall, which can kill animals and plants.	☐	☐
Using more wood for fuel could increase deforestation, which will destroy habitats for animals and plants.	☐	☐
Using more fossil fuels will decrease global warming, because burning fossil fuels releases CO_2.	☐	☐

(3 marks)

Globalisation and Food Supply

1   Study **Figure 1**, which is an article about the increase in global food demand.

Figure 1

GLOBAL FOOD DEMAND GROWING OUT OF CONTROL

Over the last 40 years there has been a large increase in the amount of food consumed globally. One of the challenges in years to come will be producing enough food to meet the ever-growing demand. More pesticides and fertilisers will need to be used to grow food in massive quantities. Producing more food will also increase the demand on water supplies — between 1980 and 2002 the area of irrigated land in the world increased by over 600 000 km^2, and this will keep growing. Many countries are importing food from around the world to meet their demands, which has caused an increase in commercial farming of cash crops in places like Brazil, Thailand and Africa.

(a) Suggest a reason for the increased global demand for food.

....

(1 mark)

(b) Using **Figure 1**, explain one impact of meeting the increased demand for food.

....

....

(2 marks)

(c) Many countries are importing food from around the world to meet the increased demand.

(i)   What term is given to the distance food is transported to its market?

....

(1 mark)

(ii)   Describe one negative impact of importing food from around the world.

....

....

(2 marks)

(d) Increased demand for imported food has caused many farmers in poorer countries to switch from subsistence farming to commercial farming.

(i)   Describe how commercial farming is different from subsistence farming.

....

....

(1 mark)

(ii)   Explain the problems caused by switching from subsistence to commercial farming.

....

....

....

(2 marks)

Reducing the Impacts of Globalisation

1   Study **Figure 1**, which shows the electricity production from renewable sources in an area.

Figure 1

	1998	2008

Total electricity generation from renewable sources = 5000 GWh

Total electricity generation from renewable sources = 12 000 GWh

Key
- Wind
- Hydroelectric power
- Biomass

(a) (i)   Using **Figure 1**, calculate the amount of electricity produced using biomass in 2008.

....
(1 mark)

(ii)   The amount of electricity produced using wind in 1998 was 1250 GWh. Calculate the difference in the amount of electricity produced using wind between 1998 and 2008.

....

....

....
(2 marks)

> Don't forget to put the units at the end of your answer.

(b) (i)   Describe how electricity can be generated using hydroelectric power.

....

....
(2 marks)

(ii)   Describe another renewable energy source that isn't mentioned in **Figure 1**.

....

....
(2 marks)

(c)   Give two reasons why renewable energy sources are sustainable.

1 ....

2 ....
(2 marks)

2   Describe a renewable energy source that you have studied and the impacts it has had.

(6 marks)

Reducing the Impacts of Globalisation

3   Study **Figure 2**, which is an extract from an article on the Kyoto Protocol.

(a)   Carbon dioxide emissions are causing global warming. Use **Figure 2** to state two effects of global warming.

Figure 2

THE KYOTO PROTOCOL

Global warming is causing sea level to rise and extreme weather events to happen more frequently. To tackle the issue, countries have signed the Kyoto Protocol. They have to monitor and cut emissions of carbon dioxide and other gases by 2012. Each country has agreed to reach an emissions target and the carbon credits trading scheme encourages them to meet their targets.

....

....

....

....
                                                              (2 marks)

(b)   Describe how the carbon credits scheme works to help reduce carbon dioxide emissions.

....

> The number of marks gives you an idea of the level of detail that's needed.

....

....

....
                                                              (4 marks)

4   Study **Figure 3**, which shows the average level of ozone (a pollutant at low altitude) in urban areas in the UK.

Figure 3

(a)   Complete **Figure 3** to show that the level of ozone in 2004 was 57 micrograms per cubic metre.
                          (1 mark)

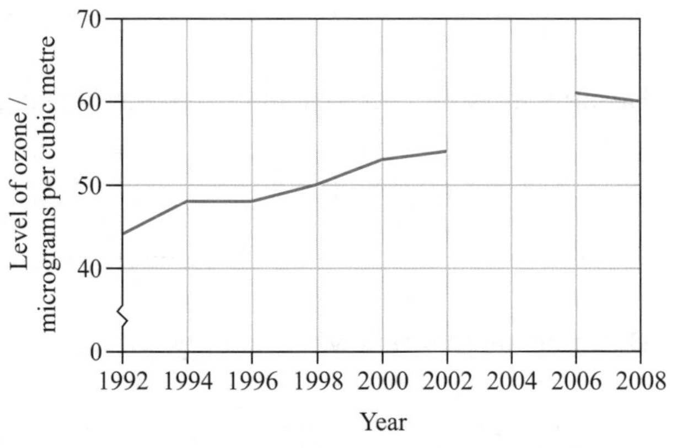

(b)   Using **Figure 3**, describe the change in the level of ozone between 1992 and 2008.

....

....
                                                              (2 marks)

(c)   Describe an international agreement to control pollution, apart from the Kyoto Protocol.

....

....
                                                              (2 marks)

Reducing the Impacts of Globalisation

5   Study **Figure 4**, which shows waste disposal methods in the different districts of a county.

(a) (i)   What percentage of the waste produced
           in Cleener was recycled?

     ....
                                                    (1 mark)

     (ii) The waste produced in Dirtdale weighed a
           total of 400 000 tonnes. Calculate the weight
           of Dirtdale's waste that was taken to landfill.

           ....

           ....
                                                    (2 marks)

Figure 4

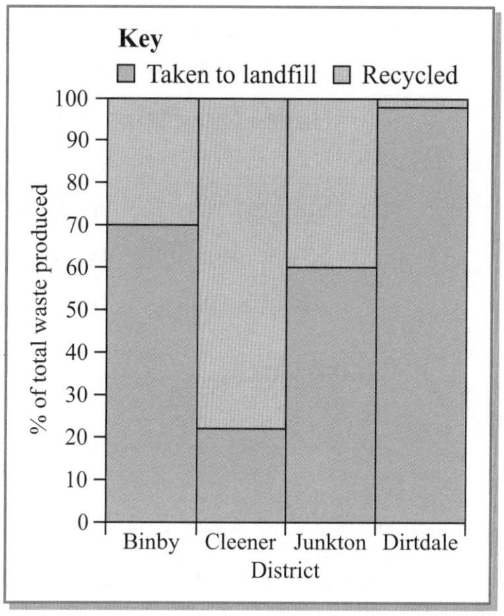

(b) Complete the paragraph below to explain the impact
     of increased globalisation on waste production.
     Choose the correct words from this list.

low	**increased**	**transporting**
recycling	**high**	**decreased**

Globalisation has given people access to more products at .... prices so people can

afford to be more wasteful. This means the amount of waste produced has .... as

globalisation has increased. .... waste reduces the amount of waste going to landfill.

                                                    (3 marks)

6   Study **Figure 5**, which shows the average amount spent per month on local produce in a town.

Figure 5

Year	1989	1994	1999	2004	2009
Amount	£8.22	£9.50	£10.80	£12.68	£16.70

(a) Using **Figure 5**, describe the change in the amount spent on local produce from 1989 to 2009.

'Using figure' means using
numbers or facts from the
figure in your answer.

     ....

     ....
                                                    (2 marks)

(b) One disadvantage of buying local produce is that it can put people in poorer countries
     who export food out of a job. Give two advantages of buying local produce.

     ....

     ....
                                                    (2 marks)

Unit 2B — Tourism

Growth in Tourism

1   Study **Figure 1**, which shows the most popular tourist destinations in Bremma.

Figure 1

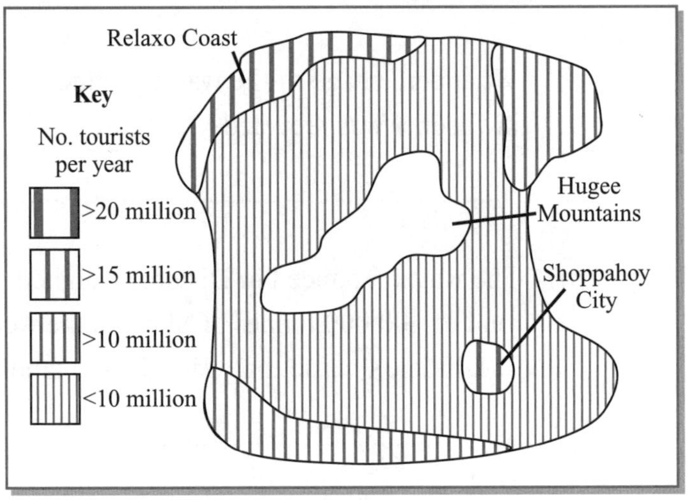

(a) (i)   Complete **Figure 1** to show that 22 million tourists visit the Hugee Mountains each year.

(1 mark)

(ii) Suggest why Relaxo Coast and Shoppahoy City are very popular with tourists.

Relaxo Coast ....

....

....

Shoppahoy City ....

....

(2 marks)

(b) Study **Figure 2**, which shows the number of visits abroad made by UK residents between 1999 and 2006. Suggest reasons for the trend shown in **Figure 2**.

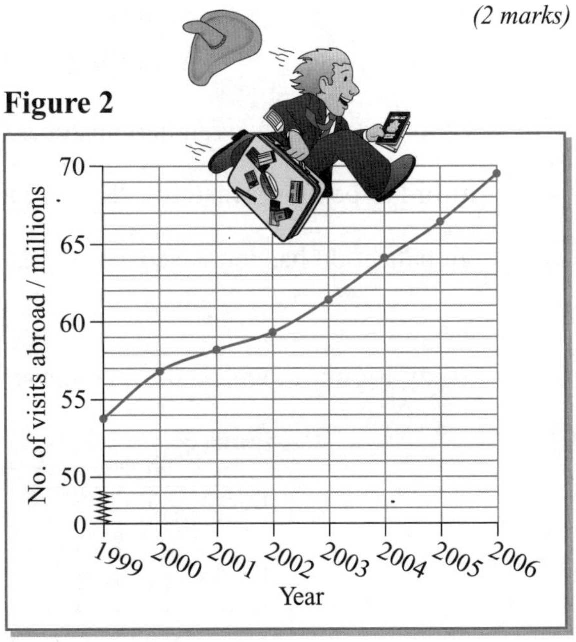

It's a four mark question, so try to come up with four reasons.

Figure 2

....

....

....

....

....

....

....

(4 marks)

(c) (i)   Give one reason why tourism is an important economic activity.

....

(1 mark)

(ii) Contrast the economic importance of tourism in rich and poor countries.

'Contrast' means write about the differences.

....

....

(2 marks)